Of No
Fixed Address

Kaizad Gustad was born in Bombay in 1968. Or at least that's what he's been told. He is a part-time writer of screenplays and short stories and a full-time traveller of more places than he'd care to remember. He is the writer/director of two short films and one feature film, *Bombay Boys*. As of this writing, he resides alone somewhere between Bombay and New York. He is not married and has no issue … that he is aware of.

Of No Fixed Address

KAIZAD GUSTAD

HarperCollins *Publishers* India

HarperCollins *Publishers* India Pvt Ltd
7/16 Ansari Road, Daryaganj, New Delhi 110 002

Copyright © Kaizad Gustad 1998

Published in hardback 1998 by
HarperCollins *Publishers* India
First in Paperback 1999
Second impression 1999

ISBN 81-7223-346-9

Cover Design: Tracy Turner/Ayesha Parakh

Typeset by
Megatechnics
19A, Ansari Road
New Delhi 110 002

Printed in India by
Gopsons Papers Ltd
A-14, Sector 60
Noida 201 301

For mom
for putting up for all these years with a son of no fixed address...

Contents

Acknowledgements

I would like to thank Michalene and Charles Milne for their early encouragement to write this book. To Rosie Daswani and William Rhode for being harsh editors, critics and friends. To Zenobia Bhappoo, Asit Chandmal and Frank Simoes for their help and support. To David Godwin, my agent, who is responsible for getting this book into print. To Sanjana Malhotra and Renuka Chatterjee at HarperCollins for being kind enough to publish it, more or less intact. And to Rumana Hamied for being so easily courted through these pages...

Meena

Her name, I later discovered, was Meena. She had those eyes. Big as the land, black as a starless night in winter. They were mascara lined, deep and alluring. They only served to mystify her uncalming appearance, her almost unnerving stillness.

It was a grimy night that we chose to drift lazily down Bombay's notorious street of cages. Officially, it's still named Falkland Street, although some unimaginative locals altered a letter or two on the sign to more closely reflect the main livelihood of the neighbourhood. The taxi drivers in the know knew it better as Shuklaji street or Kamathipura. Like voyeurs in a silent auction, they would wait to transport middle-aged men in anonymous safari suits in quickest possible time to the cages.

Meena was different. Perhaps thirteen, perhaps sixteen, it was difficult to tell behind the make-up that caked her face like multiple layers of skin, pastel-like, creased with every smile, every fluttering of the eyelashes. The lipstick job was overdone in the most headline grabbing of manners. A cheap fake import from Chor Bazaar probably — it glistened and ran with the machinations of tongues and mouths too many. It frayed itself at the edges like a bedsheet come off at the corners after a particularly volatile night. Her gaudy sari was clearly a hand-me-down from the madam of the house; a plastic imitation of the real thing, the bright red blouse stuffed with enough ambience to serve as fish and tackle for unwitting men. Chunky jewellery hung off dainty ears and fingers too fragile to hold the weight.

The car braved the tempest of throbbing crowds and pressing flesh. Drug dealers dealt out dolefuls in corners. Card sharks played games on footpaths crumbling with the weight of people. Tooth-pick mouthed pushers heaved their wares onto unsuspecting cabbies and tourists.

We were a motley bunch of five or six — teen-aged, bottle drawn, joints squeezed between fingers yellowed and stained with the passage of heavy time. We were also of that class of haves — of designer labels and fancy imports and signatured paintings hung prominently on every wall. We were the Bandra lot, the Nepean Sea Road lot, the Malabar Hill lot, the Breach Candy lot. Our neighbourhoods still retained their English namesakes whilst most around us had become Hutatma Chowk and Dadasaheb Phalke Marg. This evening we were out for a new sort of sightseeing. The house of cages and the human zoo. It was a finger-pointing session at best. A few teases washed down with a litre of London Pilsner.

I first saw Meena somewhere between the Nepali women, the soft-core porn theatre displaying gaudy white women in semi-undress, and my third Pilsner. She was leaning against the bright-red of the entrance, swinging her arms perfunctorily, a soiled curtain swaying lazily behind her. Her sari caressed her uncomfortably, almost guilty in its prematureness. All around her, old and young, dark and fair alike, lured and provoked. They ran fingers down their tattered blouses, up the hem of their hurriedly re-worn costumes. *Paan*-stained tongues came out, rolling bits of *supari* ingeniously at the tip, demonstrating ability and experience. It was a flea-market, a human bazaar, a dime and nickel used goods store, a twenty-four-hour 7-11 shop.

Meena was the sombre, sedated one. The one that sits unadorned, in some dark recess of the supermarket — sporting no fancy labels, screaming no half-price vouchers. She stared down at her Hyderabadi bangles, stolen perhaps by the madam from a cheap stall near the Char Minar. She played listlessly with them. Abstractedly. Her eyes seemed lined with permanent tears, entrapped within the definitive boundaries of her mascara.

Inside the car, we kept the horn blaring, shrieking mechanical high-pitched whistles amidst sniggers and bawdy jokes that had been recycled a hundred times. This is how the boys from finishing schools finish. From the hallowed halls of Cathedral and John Connon, to this cruising behind the tinted windows of foreign cars that fend off beggars and noise and pollution with equal vehemence.

Outside, sweaty men muscled heavy workloads in creaking shoulder-drawn transportations. Bullock-carts blocked busy intersections. Topless men sold ice, buried in blankets of sawdust. Children played marbles beside gutters, *gili-danda* on narrow municipality dug-up footpaths. We trudged on. A finger on the pane, an incense seller, ganja by the rupee, *paan* with 300 and 600-kilometre bhang, enough to keep us going as many hours. But mostly, there were the women. Mostly, there was Meena.

My gaze was hurried and withdrawn. Unsettling perhaps. Her plainness rung rings around the others. Mostly, I remember her eyes. They were darkened pools, fathomless, buried treasure and myths and cargo disappearing therein. They spoke in multitudinous volumes — in hieroglyphics. I translated every subtext, every nuance, every accent over every mono-syllable. Our eyes met but for a particle of a second. An opening of a wink, a flutter of eyelashes long and sultry, pressed against bushy eyebrows. And then we were gone and so was she, in a flurry of activity, buried amidst beggars and god-men alike. I was suddenly alone once more.

***

Sleep is a strange bedfellow. An unfaithful lover at best, it came and went and came again, like a customer at some cheap pay-by-the-hour hotel in Colaba, the ones the *firangis* frequent. Meena was everywhere I went. In dreams technicoloured and cinemascope. I had to find her again.

***

"Thin and tall, dark, with very large black eyes," I found myself repeating to the *paanwalla*. He spat the betel juice out, horizontally jet-propulsing it twenty feet or so till it splattered like an abstract painting onto a nearby wall with a "Post No Bills" sign posted onto it.

"Every other *Randi* here is like that, mister. You have cage number?"

"No," I found myself saying.

"Then you want *paan* instead mister? 300-kilometre bhang with *palang-tode* enough to keep you and little Johnny-Boy-Fandango looking through the night."

"No," I found myself saying again. The *supari* was vicious enough, the legendary aphrodisiac to go with it was a trifle too much. Besides, I wasn't looking for any of the local Fandango flavour — I had to find Meena.

I walked the length and narrow breadth of Falkland. I wondered where the name came from. "House of Cages" I could understand, not Falkland Street. It seemed altogether too English suburbia. I imagined white picket fences, chimneys, Range Rovers and dogs named Spot. This was a complete nonsequitur.

Imaginary lines of demarcation greeted every stranger on every corner. There were the Nepali houses — all sporting the fair models recently imported or smuggled. There were the Maharashtrians with saris tucked tightly into bosoms and buttocks alike. There were the *hijras*: men in drag, but without much pretense or hope of being anything other than square-jowled, broad-shouldered men in mirror-laden blouses. There were the fat ones — rolling layer upon layer of ample skin like so much dough in a cookie factory. There were the pimps and the wannabes. Broad-collared, a chewed stub of a toothpick permanently lodged into narrow cavities, and a greying Charminar filterless pasted above one ear. Each cage had its own name tag, an identity number for easy reference by gold prospectors and tax collectors alike.

I stop a pink-collared pimp — shirt out, sleeves rolled to the elbows. I explain my predicament. He looks at me and sees dollar signs in my eyes. What was I doing here? This long-tressed, wild-eyed, bohemian-clothed, somewhat of a *firangi* man wanting to know about a local call-girl? His dilated eyes gave me the once-over many times.

"I will find her for you, no problem," he tells me assuredly.

"How much?" I want to know.

He gives me the twice-over now — judging my ability to pay.

"Five hundred rupees."

"One hundred."

"Two."

We arrive at a gentleman's agreement.

"No, no I don't have her name, but she has these eyes you see..." I attempt to describe the searched.

"*Saab, saab.* Forget name. Too many names come and go. All made up. Tell me cage number."

"I don't know. If I did, you think I'd hire you?"

"*Saab. saab.* Go home *saab.* Go home. I take care of rest. I find her for you or my name not Champaran — chief first friend and looker-after of all the ladies from 230 to 290."

With those reassuring words, I left. The location, but not the search. I walked past alleyways so narrow, I had to squeeze through sideways. There were syringes and crumpled joints every so many feet. There were men in niches and alcoves, backs against walls of political graffiti. There were women on knees, in chairs, on creaking and often monotonously shivering charpoys. Dirty, crumpled rupee notes surreptitiously exchanged hands as though sleep should come less guiltless if quickly paid for. There were neighbours on second floors and children on make-shift toys. All oblivious to the goings-on around them. There were shish-kebab and biryani vendors, selling lumps of flesh less cheap than human, garnished by fancifully potent chutneys and paper-plates that succumb

to the weight. Life outside the palace gates was throbbing
— pulsating far more frenetically than tinted windows on
casual drivebys would allow.

***

A Pandu policeman, complete with loose, dangling khaki
shorts and unused shiny baton stopped me one evening.

"What you doing here?"

"None of your business."

A moment's stare, an imaginary palm held out. I
walked on. He tapped me on the shoulder with the baton.
I turned around.

"What you doing here?" he repeated.

"Looking for a girl."

"It is illegal."

I laughed. A costly mistake as I was to later find out
at the station.

The back of the police van is exactly as I thought it
would be from seeing too many Hindi movies. He stopped
a short distance from the station and walked around to
the rear.

"Where do you live?"

"Nowhere around here."

"I'll take you home if..."

"If?"

"If..."

I looked at him with all the quizzical naïveté of a
stranger to the land. The outstretched hand wasn't so
imaginary after all.

"If you... make up for your sins."

"How?"

"Fifty rupees and your parents won't know."

"They already do."

"Hundred rupees and the Chief Inspector won't know."

"I don't care."

The Chief Inspector listened to my story with incredulity writ large across his ample face. Incredulity at my desire to find her. He stumbled over words and semantics, grasping for appropriate sentences. Eventually, all that uttered itself was "Why?"

"I don't know," I replied.

I could have said it was the eyes, the sadness, the way she held her head, the way she played nonchalantly with her bangles. I could have said one of many explanations, but they all seemed too trifling and somehow unnecessary.

"What is her name?"

"I don't know."

"What is her number?"

"I do not know," once again.

"Is she legal, is she above age, is she licensed, is she, or isn't she?"

The sure-fire staccato questions kept pouring its cumulative venom at me. "Why, why, why?" I looked away. I refused to co-operate any more. The police bureaucracy makes red tape look decidedly bloody. I refused on grounds of my right to privacy from releasing my home address and telephone number — from even giving my name. I examined pot-bellies large and oval and plateau-like. It is the first test to becoming a policeman in India. "And pray tell me, how large is thy stomach?" I watched polished boots to spit on. I saw criminals and crooks and innocents hurried away into ante-rooms filled with smoke and ugly bulbs and broken blinds. I saw officers dozing, boots on tables in air-conditioned "computer rooms", newspapers folded over their faces at the crime pages. I drifted with the lazy talk and stale gossip. He looked at me now — point-blank, and twitched his thumb and forefinger in the universal sign-language that reads *"Baksheesh"* in any currency.

I was damned if I was to give this obese policeman any corrupt money. I shook my head, smiled, and politely said 'No'.

I cooled my heels that night in a slammer with a few stereotypical pimps, a card shark and a bootlegger from the Dharavi slum. We all lay there like bodies in a mortuary, staring at the suckings and slaps of tiny lizards as they scrawled their ominous way around the ceiling. Every so often, one would fall to the ground with a sickening thud, and lie there mortified; gravity-ridden like the rest of us. In the morning, better sense prevailed.

Parents came with shock expressed in capital neon letters. Monies exchanged hands and I was quick-too-quick bundled out before the Polaroid was taken for proof.

Days later, it was business as usual at the crack of first dawn in the Irani restaurants. The tea was served piping hot in tiny fingerprint-stained glasses with a slice too many of the crisp, freshly-made *Broom-Pao*, layered with a myriad inches of butter. Drunks were stumbling their way out of cages, booted out after a welcome overstayed. I walked past the Nepali house, already open for business. I walked past the slumbering *hijras*, past row upon row of bare bottoms doing their do on footpaths, against open gutters. I turned corners, I walked past and down and through once again, until it was just one long unidentifiable street.

Every cage I stopped at, I was pulled and provoked. I lost shirt buttons and sunglasses and explained lipstick marks on collars every night at home. Finally, that morning, I found Champaran — the ladies looker-after. Or rather, he found me.

"*Saab. saab*. I found. I found. Come with me. Number 269. Here. Right here." He took me, hand to elbow to the cage number.

"But first, I need payment."

"How I so sure it is her?" I ask.

"You sure. Trust me, or my name not Champaran, ladies looker-after number one chief assistant. Satisfaction guaranteed or ask anyone here for Champaran and you get your money back."

I hand over the money without counting. He's impressed.

The cage did look like the one where I thought I had seen her. He led me through the curtains and introduced me to the madam, collecting his share from both corners. I was escorted through a labyrinthine passage. I fought past groping hands, ducked protruding tongues and heaving bosoms, ignored entrapments and promises and bargains galore. Fighting hands off back pockets all the way up the rickety stairs, I passed cubicles of beds, and dormitories of rugs and sleeping coir mats with bodies entwined like snapshots from the Kama Sutra. I opened every cardboard enclosement, I peered through every muslin sheet, every gaping hole along the way. She was nowhere.

The madam of the house rested her well-rolled frame against a dark wood panelled wall adorned with goddesses of wealth and fame, death and power. Incense burned by the window. It was a small, cramped room, heady with smell and prestige and burdened by too many secrets. She rolled and heaved her way every breath or so into more comfortable positions, plucking at her bra-straps every so often, re-arranging them to support vast dunes that invading armies on camels could march across and get lost in. She fiddled with a box of *pan-parag*, flicking the tiny morsels into a bottomless, cavernous mouth, with open palms stained by much expertise and *mehndi* alike.

"How much?" she asks, point-blank.

"I ... erm... just want to talk to her."

"How much?"

"To talk?"

"How much?"

"Ten... twenty rupees?"

"Twenty minutes."

"Where is she?"

An honest palm protrudes. I deposit a shiny new twenty rupee note. She is pleased.

"Wait here."

She left. I was alone. Kali and Durga and other women with long hair and longer tongues swathed in the blood of killed prey stared down at me from their pedestals. The incense was making me heady with nonsense. It was an unusual smell. Intoxicating. Ten minutes later, a girl entered. I could see even through her veil it was not Meena.

***

It was one week, and almost four hundred rupees later that I saw her again. She stood exactly where I had first seen her. It was a freeze-frame of sorts, a snapshot tattooed into permanence. Her stance, her clothes, her look, those eyes, the bangles, the withering vulnerability of it all. Nothing was any different. It was the night I first saw her all over again.

I walked hesitantly and stood before her. Her eyes barely flinched a muscle, yet she seemed somehow to acknowledge my presence. She turned quietly on a soft heel and with a gentle murmur of her *ghungroo*, led me inside. The madam looked me up and down, uncertain as to the charge. I pressed a few ten-rupee notes into her well-garnished palms. She tucked them comfortably out of sight, down the neck of her blouse. We entered a room, postage-stamp sized. The door hit the edge of the bed and we had to enter askew.

She sat at one end of the bed, atop a stubborn lumpy swelling in the naked coir mattress. Her head down, she stared at the cheap imitation *ghungroo* garlanding her ankle. She sat still and upright, playing aimlessly with her bangles, moving them up and down her slender wrists, as though wishing to gently tease the skin below. It seemed as though she was bemoaning the physical trappings simply as the unfortunate consequences of unimaginative minds. I stood, back against the door, watching like a child that opens its eyes for the very first time and screams a scream rooted in nine months of numbing paraplegic blindness.

I sat eventually. At the other end. Looking at her. My mind kept racing with unwarranted questions. I needed something tangible, some physical hook on which to peg my unqualified search and therein explain its consequences. A birthmark? A mole? A beauty spot? An eyeline? Fingers perhaps? A look? A demeanour? No. There was nothing.

I do not know how long a time it was that passed. We both sat there, motionless; making mockery of theorems of revolving earths and solar systems in constant orbit. Now, there was nothing but stillness. And silence. Even the anonymously soothing chatter of her bangles ceded to silence. Her *ghungroo* lay stripped naked of its

bells. She looked at her feet, at the floor, at the wall —
over every conceivable dimension of the room save that
which I occupied.

I stopped looking, stopped the inquisition, leaving the
questions unanswered. Words were too redundant to
imagine, thoughts too verbose to think. She, the odalisque
of an unforgiving world, I the unwitting voyeur with one
eye glued permanently to the keyhole. There was no
common ground. I allowed myself to dwarf emotions, to
withdraw guilt and shame and all the other trappings of
my world. For once, I allowed myself, only in her
presence, somehow, to just be. She permitted this. A
return, foot-to-the-pedal and highway-bound, back to
kilometre zero.

An hour. Perhaps two. A knocking. A gentle wait, lest
intrusions were ill-timed. A door opening. A subtle look
at customer and client imagining things unhappened. I
left.

***

We sat by the waters of the Arabian Sea, on that strip
of Bombay known as Marine Drive by day, and the
Queen's Necklace by night. We watched the murky grey
of the waters recede into a low-tide, allowing the debris
to remain behind. We watched the ships merge clumsily
into the sky, the sun dip vehemently and turn its face
away, onto pastures new.

She sat dangling her feet off the ledge, savouring the
somewhat burned *bhutta* with a touch too much of lime
and chilli powder. I watched her in her simple glee as
she extracted with her fingers a stubborn ear of corn
lodged between her teeth. I listened to the bangles catch
the air and make gentle music.

***

We eat *bhelpuri* at Chowpatty and wash it down with ice-cold *malai kulfi*. We go out to the lamp-lit beach and step over bodies being massaged by nimble fingers and scalding hot coconut oil. She holds her sandals in her hands and teases the sand into flight. I think I hear her laugh.

We bribe the *tonga-wallah* to take his horse-chariot to the far end of Marine Drive, towards all those glistening skyscrapers and back again via Tardeo to the cages. He is not too pleased with the latter itinerary, nor the obvious lineage of his cargo, but allows a crisp note to change his mind.

No sooner are we off than she stands up in the open air and allows the balmy breeze to blow her untied hair and *dupatta* in the wind. I sit below and watch the smile spread cautiously, and somewhat guiltily across her face.

The madam inspects her thoroughly, like one would a race horse at point of purchase. Teeth, mane, nails, ears, muscles. She all but spreads her fingers and spans her length. Satisfied with the goods returned in working order, she nods at me, and I leave. I walk out backwards, ignoring the taunts and teases of puppy love, even as a hirsutely rotund man with crooked, brown *paan*-stained teeth examines his ten rupees' worth.

I stop a taxi across the street and ask the driver to put the metre down and let me stay in the back seat. He is somewhat pleased with the lazy money, and saunters off window-shopping with his advance. I stare out at her cage, cups of dirty brown coffee in finger-stained glasses to keep me company through an awake and restless night.

***

We went everywhere together. The Hanging Gardens of Malabar Hill, the ice-cream parlours of Breach Candy, the hills and waterfront streets of Bandra. We saw three-hour long Hindi movie extravaganzas, monkey-tricks by the Taj Hotel, and visited the Apollo Circus when it came to town. We did all there was to do in Bombay without ever saying a word, or holding a hand.

***

I do not remember how long a time it was that passed before I had to leave again. I do not remember where it was I was leaving for. I just remember having to leave. When I saw her the last time, we sat on the same lumpy bed, much as we did the first time, and I kept prolonging the inevitable by feeding the hungry madam's palms until there was nothing left — not even the ride back home. I do not remember how it was that she knew I was leaving. Still — she betrayed nothing, much as I expected her to.

When the final knock arrived, there was nothing left to do. I felt it was time to ask her her name.

"Meena," she said.

Just the way I thought she would.

****

An Angel at the Garden

This is the way it isn't — tropical weather, penthouse suite, harbour views, frozen Daquiri, Krug in a bucket, and Angel in bed between black satin sheets.

This is the way it is — hot and stickily humid, ground floor flat in a large residential complex in Kowloon, parking lot views, semi-cold Tsing Tao beer, no Krug in a bucket and Angel stuffing tiny bound feet into stubbornly prescription airline stockings, complaining loudly in Cantonese about the run in the right leg.

Me, I don't know. I don't know what in Fung Shui's name I'm doing here blocking the mountains from seeing the sea. The parking lot at Telford Gardens has an interesting quality to it when viewed with a certain light. I can see the shiny new steel of the MTR line wind its slow way out of the mountain and into daylight as it approaches Kowloon Bay station.

Angel is off again. To Vancouver or Paris or Taipei I don't know. Her Cathay Pacific shoes pinch in all the right places, and the stockings she hates with a passion. "Makes me look too fat, no?" she worries in her halting English. Angel, fat? I don't know. Depends on where you come from. She's 90 pounds in your part of the world, about 40 kilos here. Me, I think the Buddha's fat, but I don't tell her.

Besides, he's Indian, not Oriental, dark-skinned and swarthy. But I don't tell her that either.

***

I have come to Mong Kok to flex the culinary. Angel weaned me towards drunk shrimps that dance merrily on your plate. She introduced me to comatose prawns and mussels you have to use a prying lever to get out. I see the little things heaved onto a vat of boiling water. I use prongs and sticks and other inducements to ferry them out onto a salivating tongue. I swallow snake soup in gulpfuls even though it is not yet winter. I know the stuff works like tonic. I have been in search of the gall bladder a few days now but it is in short supply. I have to make a trip to Sham Shui Po, where the stuff is pierced out of lively wriggling snakes by human teeth and paraded to bystanders, sold to the highest bidder. It is early August and all of Hong Kong has wrapped itself in its usual blanket of sweat, misery and fraying tempers.

It will be six days before she returns. I will be there at Kai Tak as usual. I'll have taken the 5D from the Telford terminal, dropped a few sink washers into the coin machine and gotten off at the airport stop. I will wait there patiently the five or fifty minutes it will take her and her giggling cohorts to exit down the ramp and towards me, waiting with the usual stolen red flower from Amoy Gardens. I will be introduced to them one more time as usual, an exercise purely at my discomfort every time, and done only for that purpose.

"This he. Hee-hee-hee. My friends. Veronica, Cupid, Dusky, Farrow and me, of course you know, Angel. Hee-hee."

At which point Veronica, Cupid, Dusky and Farrow will laugh their ubiquitous hee-hees and shyly make their many splendoured exits towards the crew lounge in the BMWs of Anglo pilot husbands, or the nondescript airline buses of poor local boyfriends. I have never figured out this introduction. Every flight. The same thing. Only the names change.

"Hee-hee. My boyfriend. This Angel, not me, part two, hee-hee, and Adonis, Venus and Oesophagus."

That last I made up of course. But you get the picture.

***

It is boiled Won Tons again, in yesterday's dishwater. I haven't figured this thing out either. It's always the same. Won Ton. Six days in Paris and the urge for the humble Won Ton is unbearable. Seven days in Vancouver (Vankong or Hongcouver as they call it) and enough is enough. Gimme my Won Ton. Ditto for London. Only worse. Angel is going through her multi-currency FCNR passbook account maintained diligently since her first flight at the local branch of the Hang Seng bank. She gulps whole Won Tons even as she talks.

"You think I should switch to Hong Kong?"

"You are in Hong Kong, " I stutter.

"No. No. To Hong Kong bank."

"Why?"

"They only give me 12.8 on my AUD account and the yen is no good either."

"If you think so."

"What you think?"

"Whatever you want. It's your money."

"OK, if you say so."

"No I just said that ...". I give up. It's no use. "How many accounts have you got?"

"One. With deposits in nine currencies. Dollar, pound, yen, franc, ECU, mark..."

"What's an ECU?"

"I don't know. But I got 2,642 of them."

"Good for you."

"Tomorrow I switch to Hong Kong Bank. Won Ton good, no?"

The next night we go to the Wong Tai Sin temple to read our future in a joss stick. We reach the MTR and search for money to feed hungry machines, but she hasn't any, and I never have. We go over to the Hong Kong bank ATM machine in Telford and get in line behind seventeen people. Across, we can see two in line for the Hang Seng one. I pretend not to notice. An efficient thirty-four minutes later, we are back at the MTR. We feed crisp ten dollar bills into the machine and get one way fares.

Inside, I could eat off the floor. It is shiny and scrubbed with the stench of a newly inaugurated hospital in Clearwater Bay perhaps, the type where old *Gweilo* China hands go to get their valves fixed.

***

I rattle and hum the quiver of sticks marked with Chinese lettering. I have come to recognise a few already. I do not remember how many times before I have been here at her insistence, and every time our future is different as though malleable to the whims and fancies of inanimate sticks with powers unmerciful to the truth. I shake and rattle the many sticks until one is precariously close to falling off. I can read from the inscription that this is a stick I have been dealt before, so I calmly nudge it back into place and begin again. Futures are very flexible in this part of the world.

I pull out the one that has fallen, and hand it over nonchalantly to the head priest and translator — the adumbrator of things to come. Angel does so too, with much intimidation, and respect. The old hag of a lady, wrinkled so far as to require a complete ironing and dry-cleaning, shakes her head in a manner I know does not bode well.

"He will leave you," she translates. "No good. Much restlessness. No good. Plenty travel for both. No good. No good lines here. No good. No future. No future at all. No good."

It was no good all right. Whichever way I looked at it.

***

Me, I can't figure out the whole damn thing. I've been taking Cantonese lessons every Thursday night. I know how to tell the bus driver "*Tak Fak Fa Yoon*" to get me home, and "*Kok Thaiy Thai Aah*" to go pick her up from the crew lounge. I know her friends' names by heart which says a lot, all things considered, and have even memorised the occasional word in the Mandarin she speaks to show off. I know just how to prepare her Won Tons, and where to get gall bladder and Peking Duck cheaper than in Peking. I know every back alley and road and gully from the New Territories to the Peak, and even manage to take her a place or two she hasn't seen.

I call her collect in Zurich or Sapporo or Rome or wherever she happens to be flying to, and tell her how much I love her in Cantonese and Mandarin and English and Chinglish combined. I know the hotel number of the Narita Prince by heart, the Concorde in Paris, the Oberoi in Bombay. I can flash country codes and city codes in a zap. I can add and subtract time zones on the tips of my fingers and know when she's sleeping and when she's eating and when she's doing both. I always take the 5D to Kai Tak and bring her back safely even if she goes on a turnaround to Manila or Bangkok. I listen patiently to all her stories and comparisons of discotheques in participating hotels.

I know by heart the allowance she makes in each city. I can convert the sterling to the Australian dollar, the yen to the US in a moment. I can understand the ramifications of pegging 7.8 Hong Kong dollars to 1 US, and can sympathise when the mark drops due to political instability. I even know the different percentages of interest she gets from all her various accounts, agreeing that 12.9 on the AUD is better than 12.8 and never mind the thirty-four minutes. Still, I can't figure the thing out.

She, been here all her life. Finished grade school in a public education, somewhere in Kowloon Tong, cramped thirty-three to a classroom, learning English all wrong. Sixteen, and she works two years in a local 5 star hotel (not the Peninsula or the Mandarin Oriental, but close) learning the various ropes of the service industry. Her ambition as far back as she can remember was to see the world on someone else's money. She waits till she's nineteen to qualify for an application to someone else.

Fails the first on account of poor skin, she says. Dejected and down on her luck, she withdraws for months on end, her life's dream vaporised by the inadequacies of a cheap dermatologist from Wanchai. Still, with the pluck and fortitude of her blood, she tries again and much haggling and back-bitching later, manages an entrée to free flight. Two years maybe, she first said to herself. See the world and then move on.

Six years later and she's still stuck. Velcroed by easy access to foreign boyfriends, familiar hotel rooms and the hard currency of nine countries. She's gone from Economy to First Class she points out. No more fly-by-night shuttles to Dubai catering to cheap drunks and bawdy Arabs. Now its strictly first class all the way. Customers she knows of, and addresses in flight by last name only. The Jardine Fleming crowd she calls them. The index to the Hang Seng. The denizens of the Peak, the white-walled bungalows of the Mid Levels and the oil blue of Clearwater and Repulse Bays. She's moving up and on all right. Only, she wants no excess baggage in flight. Or on ground.

I'm travelling excessively light these days.

***

We meet outside the Happy Luck Fortune Dynasty Company building in Causeway Bay. She has come here to pick me up from my job in a local underground newspaper. The evening is sweltering under the weight of six million people marching to familiar destinations, one ear glued to portable phones. She has been waiting half an hour with the patience of a foreign observer at an old women's Mah-jong game. I slip out of the building dazed by the evening heat, in shorts and torn shirt, holding the newspaper under my arm.

"Let me see your name," she begins the familiar routine again.

"I told you — no name."

"Why? You journalist or not?"

"Yes. But I don't want anyone to know."

"Why not?"

"I told you why not. I'm a wannabe writer, not a hack copy writer. Me, a journalist? I'd rather be a whore on Temple Street."

"They don't get much. Besides, you not that pretty."

"I'd open my own multi-currency account. In Hong Kong Bank."

"No good. The pound rate too low."

"I'll only accept yen."

"Devalued yesterday at closing."

"I give up."

"Good. Let's go home."

I don't want to repeat to her that the real reason I can't have my by-line in the papers is that I don't have my work visa yet. In two weeks I have to take the KCR train to mainland China again and get another three months' extension. That night I look at my passport. It is cluttered and dog-eared with a high school photograph and I cannot find my China visa. When I do, I realise it is for a single entry only, and is no good. Another trip to Cheung King Mansions in Tsim Sha Tsui to get a three-day visa job done dirt cheap. I count the China visas. Four already. I have been here almost fifteen months. Now I know.

Me, I can't figure what I'm doing here learning Cantonese, playing with Joss sticks, drinking snake soup, catching the MTR, taking the STAR ferry and the Peak Tram and twice every week the 5D. True, I can't figure what I'm doing here, except it has been home for thus long, surely it can't be all bad? Truth be told, it has grown on me like an ulcerous gargoyle grows on the forehead. I look at it and cannot but love to hate it. Yet, it is part and parcel of the package, and for better or worse I have become comfortably accustomed to it. Angel Wong, notwithstanding the name, I have grown to love, Won Tons and all.

***

"Dirty Indians," she says with a grimace as we make our way past the various handouts and business cards that greet us at the lobby of this urban ghetto. *Taj Mahal restaurant,* one proclaims in bold pink offset. *The jewel of Indian restaurants. Room 806. Building C. Mention this business card and get 5 per cent off.* We get in line for the elevator, behind a Scandinavian couple complete with backpack and map. The thin doors open and the squeeze is on. We are the last to enter, and the buzz goes off angrily. Too much weight. The others stare at us. We promptly get off, she with much cursing — "*Yao mo Gauchuaah!*"

We get in line again and watch as the elevator rises tediously all sixteen floors, stopping at each, both ways. The lobby is a bazaar of pirated goods, and cheap memoirs from foreign lands. She stares at everything with much dismay.

"Here Grand Hyatt, there Holiday Inn, over there Peninsula, I tell you. Then of course neon of Nathan Road, and here, in the middle of all this — Cheung King. Why don't they just tear it down?"

"Where will all the poor *Gweilo* tourists go?" I muse.

"Back home," she retorts.

Argument ended, we wait for the elevator, straining necks, watching descending numbers. Finally, the doors open and we enter, cramped foetus-like, ten to a box of sardines. We get off on the sixteenth floor and walk up the one flight to the seventeenth. (Apparently, the architect couldn't figure how to get the elevator to the seventeenth floor without making a hole in the roof.) We go to the tiny travel agency and fill out papers. Reason for entry? I look at Angel.

She has that demure look I remember seeing when I first met her. I was on a flight to nowhere in particular and she served me the unopenable packet of peanuts. Wherever it was I was going, before flight's end, I knew I would end up in Hong Kong. I have been here too long, always just one step ahead of immigration.

Taking the hour-long train ride to the mainland was tantamount to leaving the country, and so a new stamp of three-month approval was permitted with each re-entry. Previously, I took the slow boat to Macao, gambled the night away, and got just the same result. Now, wiser souls in London had smartened up a bit, given the due intricacies of the British bureaucracy, and mainland China was deemed permissible, Macao not. Me, I remember meeting Angel like it were yesterday. Only it's not.

She pays the fee in newly delivered red $100 bills, crisp with starch and guilt. I cannot yet imagine why. Four times now, and every time it is the same — too afraid of losing what she doesn't want.

***

I had low-tea in China. Guangzhou to be precise. I returned via the afternoon train. The immigration officer was not pleased. I was sent to an interior room and cross-examined by three black-suited lean and taut Hong Kong immigration officers and one fat one. All I could think of was that he was the first fat Hong Konger I had seen in fifteen months. They don't grow them fat here, although God knows they eat enough. They questioned me again and again, asking redundant questions as to purpose of fifth visit, reason to stay all the three months, etc., etc. I kept thinking of the fat guy and his three thin friends. It was almost surreal, what with the hot arc lights, the green amber walls, the stark minimalism of the room, and the three thin guys and the one fat one all pointing fingers. We are in a B-grade Italian neo-realist movie from the 50's — the kind that has the subtitles spelled all wrong.

They do not allow me the one phone call when I cannot argue my case any longer, or do not want to. Whichever it is, I am alone in a detention room that night, locked and jailed as a threat to all western civilisation as we know it, for the crime of possessing an unfavourable jacket cover on my passport.

In the morning, Angel is summoned, and she appears guilty as the last Governor about to hand over the crown jewels to the natives. She explains in perfectly impassionate Cantonese why I must be allowed to stay and why she will personally fend for me and be responsible for every deed and whim and bet lost by me at the Happy Valley racecourse. Somehow, they seemed mollified, and after an hour of cheap bargaining, they give me a week's exeat only — and a confirmation number for a seat on the first available one way flight back to nowhere land, visa or not.

That night, I think of the fat guy even as Angel cannot help but weep. Her tears, like her feet, were taught to be bound and constricted from birth. What perfect decorum. They flow in contained bursts, slowly making their way down her pale cheeks. Me, I still don't understand. The fat guy is speaking Italian, only the translation is all screwed up.

***

She reports sick at the local doctor in the complex. He gives her three days. She has three guaranteed days off after that, so she hopes to make it a straight run through to departure. We sit and stare all day. It seems pointless to even attempt work. I look at her tiny frame and wonder aloud at her hopeless devotion. To what, I cannot understand. Not the passport surely? She has just seen how favourable it was; it wouldn't get her out of a pickle with the jar open. It wasn't my job, or lack thereof. It couldn't have been the temporary insanity of an August heat wave. She was with me all through winter. She wants solace now, but I haven't any to give. I stare at the palpable heat outside my window. In the distance, I can hear airplanes land and take off. The road below is screeching its weight under too many cars and car horns. The noise is a constant decibel over tolerance.

On the third day, crew control calls her out on a changed schedule. She flies unhappily on a quick turn-around to Taipei, and returns heavy set with fatigue. The next night, we have a guaranteed off, and so we take the MTR to Central and walk to the Peak tram. We reach the top and begin a slow circuitous perambulation around the fog-encrusted hill. Below, the city shimmers with promise. It is a shiny new testament to will; a neon, glass and stainless steel quiver of arrows pointed skywards. I am looking down at it for what I know will be the last time, but she can only look at the ground below. It is a fright too chilly up here, especially given the humidity of the city on a hotly trapped night.

"She was right, the old woman," I offer as weak coffee to a hangover.

She doesn't say a word. We have almost reached the Observatory again, before she stutters something faintly.

"I never believed anything she said. Don't know why I kept going there."

"But she was right this time."

"It's not your fault."

"It is."

"Why?"

"I don't know. It just is."

She wants to know if I love her, she asks me. I pluck a flower and begin ripping petals. "Love her. Love her not. Love her. Love her not. Love her..." Half way through the process, I throw the thing away. She picks it up ferociously and stares at me with much venom. She plucks away at each remaining petal, one at a merciless time.

"Love me. Love me not. Love me. Love me not." There are no petals left. She stares at the hapless stalk angrily, then begins ripping it in tiny shreds, one piece at a time. "Love me. Love me not. Love me..."

***

She, one day to go and it's standby time. That forever state of limbo sitting by the phone, staring at trudging hands on wall clocks and silent telephones, expecting to be called out at the last minute. Me, I am playing with my nails. I have nothing else to do. I think of the time I arrived here, and of the many months we spent now glorified somehow in a state of memorabilia.

I remember Ocean Park with Dusky Ng and Lisa Lee.

It was last summer, and I had been here barely a few months. The temperature had risen to almost 40 centigrades in the shade, and goodwill was in short supply. She had a standby till 9 a.m., and the four of us sat glued to the phone, concentrating all energies on seeing that it didn't ring. Two minutes past the hour and we're in the train bound for Admiralty. Dusky and Lisa and she are like urban female musketeers of the perpetually giggling kind. They stare at everything, mostly me, and giggle shamelessly.

At the park, and I'm down to next to nothing, but they have swimsuits under T-shirts. They giggle even as they step out in them, parading skin-flint legs and soles tired from too many aisles at 30,000 feet. I am impressed by their bashfulness. There is something quaintly old-fashioned about it.

We make love in the Raging Waters Pool surrounded by tides every ten minutes or so, building to an artificial, but very controlled and pragmatic high. There are lifeguards every twenty feet, and a hundred thousand people in the pool all rising and swaying with the tide, the girls giggling for all they're worth and more, the boys taking full advantage of obstructed views. Dusky sees us and is somewhat appalled. We are but twenty feet from her, and still she knows the tide can't possibly be making that much motion. She gives me that "how could you?" look. I reply with a "very easily" glance. Dusky is furious by now, and I know the publicness of the act has nothing to do with it. Her stares are pointed and vicious, and when I do not respond, she storms out of the pool.

I remember Angel very well that day. That particular day. She is fragile. Always has been. Very fragile. She smiles a lot and I respect that, even though I can't figure

why. There is a plainly innocuous simplicity about her.
She hears about the Vietnamese boat people crammed
a thousand to one in detention centres, and she feels sorry
for them, even readily offering up a tear or two. She is
told the next day what a strain on the local economy they
are, and she spouts rhetoric about how the rest of the
world should also be helping to take care of "these
people". She rages furiously at taxi drivers who won't
stop to pick up an alien fare, then justifies their fears. She
sympathises with the plight of the thousands of Philippino
maids working for next to nothing, then explains why she
hates Manila flights working with "those people".

She rounds up all her telephone bills to the next
highest number and the difference goes every month to
local charities. The Sunshine Foundation. The Hold-Your-
Hands-Across-The-World Organisation. Thirty-two cents
here, four dollars there, it all adds up.

Every month she pays her Flight Union dues of fifty
dollars and argues with herself incessantly on the necessity to do so. (If she gets laid off for whatever reason,
the Union will pay her salary.) She multiplies fifty by
twelve months times six years and realises the total
amount she's spent on them is less than what she might
get even if she did get laid off, which was unlikely, unless
she put on too much weight.

She stuffs herself with chocolate eclairs from Tokyo,
bon-bons from Paris, and then starves herself of food for
two days. She is very conscious about putting on weight.
One kilo is enough to warrant no food for a week.

She goes to Zurich for ten days and sees every nook
and cranny and crevice and trough of all Switzerland and
when she returns I tell her the name of its capital city.
I tell her about its neutrality, its 500-year anniversary

celebrated the week she was there. She shows me snapshots of smiling faces and alpine hills. Mostly, about Angel, she is always smiling.

Me, don't ask me why. She sees the tiny turrets and holes-in-the-walls that most live in and she says a little prayer. We walk past the Walled City of Kowloon and she says twenty. She is happy for her little lot in this world. I have never seen anyone so gay and for less reason.

Dusky kept quiet all the way back and so did Angel. Neither could figure out why. Lisa tried to cheer everyone up by cracking Cantonese jokes heard on TVB's "Enjoy Yourself Tonight" program. But nothing worked. We get to Dusky's home in the same complex, Block G, and she fetches bowls of Nissin 2-minute noodles and still nothing cheers them up. Then Dusky gets called out in the first five minutes of her standby for a Frankfurt, and although she doesn't want to go, is somewhat relieved. It is late, and so I volunteer the escort on the 5D. Angel looks at me rather disconcertedly. She knows I look forward to the 5D Express to the airport about as much as a partial lobotomy and doesn't let her displeasure go unnoticed. We leave hurriedly, nevertheless.

***

We stare at the phone. Become so accustomed to the noise, the silence surprises us with its viciousness.

"Remember the time we went to Ocean Park?" I offer as some communication on an archaic line in a remote village.

There is no answer. I try again.

"How about the time we first went to Wong Tai Sin and the old lady said we must marry right away?"

She smiles.   A weak smile camouflaged by much unction.

"That was the only time," she offers. "After that ...."

"I know."

Silence.   She takes people she doesn't believe too seriously for my liking.

"Remember the time I called you up in your hotel room in Jakarta and this man picked up the phone?"

"We've gone through this already.   He was Lisa's friend."

"I know, but you remember I never talked to you for one week after?"

"How could I forget?"

"So I'm gone now. Whammo. Poof. Abracadabra and all that jazz. I'm outta here. You don't need to put up with me."

"You do have a point," she proffers with a small smile.

"You didn't have to agree so readily."

"Remember when Chris called from around the corner and said he was on his way up?"

"Your ex?"

"Yes. For some reason I called you. I don't know why.   I hadn't seen him in years and then suddenly he shows up and I go and call you as though reporting for standby."

"I left work and came home."

"You never trusted me."

"Never."

"I remember you rang the bell and I sprang to the door in a mili-second to open it."

"Guilty minds."

"Suspicious minds."

"I know."

"Me too."

We've run out of steam. We both know its over, even though we make promises to stay in touch and write and meet over clandestine dinners in strange ports-of-call.

"We'll stay in touch, no?"

"Yes."

"Promise?"

"Promise."

We stay up all night. I don't remind her that the standby finished hours earlier.

***

It is morning across Telford Gardens. We go to the 7-11 and buy some coffee. We pass rows of elderly men and women doing their Tai-Chi routines. We cross the fish market, already heady with stench. We buy the newspaper for no apparent reason, as if to consolidate and confirm the date on it. We look up at the lime-green and pale tennis-ball yellow of the buildings. From Block A to M and on. We walk across the little bridge, over three starving goldfish in a dirty pond, and I wonder aloud the pomposity of the person who dared call this place a garden. We sit on a bench a while and hold hands. We watch the noise and flow of the nearby school as the snotty kids parade in obnoxiously, only to immediately sedate themselves upon entry. We take everything in as though for the first time.

On the 5D, we are standing at the rear, my one bag crammed between our legs, hoping to keep it standing. We haven't spoken a word in I don't know how long. The bus winds its concrete way through narrow roads and dug-up earth, under flyways and highways and over tunnels. I marvel one last time at the architecture of a place that has managed to extract soil from water, space from air. We watch silently as a pair of upturned winglets glide their way past precariously hung clothes-lines, barely over the top of most roofs, nipping an antenna or two along the way, as the aircraft motions itself down the runway, built into the sea. How many times have we arrived together on that one runway, I ponder aloud, only now to leave alone.

Everyone knows her here. We breeze through check-in and get a free upgrade. I am almost at customs, ready to go through the entrance. I turn around and look at her. We stand a foot apart, barely conceding movement. Then she hugs me with a borrowed warmth, from out of hidden reserves.

"I've spoken to Dominica. She's operating. She'll take good care of you. If you need anything...."

I nod.

"Call me when you reach."

I nod again.

"We'll stay in touch won't we?"

I nod once again.

Then I turn around and leave through the gate, without looking back. Me, I know I'll never see her again.

***

I ignore the brown-uniformed officer motioning me to move through the metal detectors. I count to infinity, then turn around to see her. She is gone. I breathe deeply, then scrape out the same way I got in. I head for the taxi stand, knowing she'll be in line for the bus.

"*Tak Fak Fa Yoon*. Block G."

Dusky Ng is happy to see me — finally.

****

Phaedrus and the Funny
Papers

$\mathcal{M}$rs. Weatherbeater was not usually a tempestuous woman. So when it came to pass that Sunday morning that she flung her favourite pot of gardenias through the plate glass window of her house in a quiet London suburb, many questions were on my mind.

***

I didn't exactly fit in with the family picture. Somehow I had gotten hold of this book with addresses of families that took in visitors to London for a brief period of time in their homes. Running a finger down the list, I was brought to an abrupt halt by the Weatherbeaters. Surely, in London, if they could do that, where else would I want to be, I thought?

The reply to my inquiry about boarding with them promptly came back, single-spaced, typed with an old typewriter. An occasional alphabet or two jumped off the line and hit the ones above. The Weatherbeaters would be happy to receive me it stated, and I was to wire them in advance of my arrival so that they might pick me up from the terminal.

It was a grimy 6 o'clock on a weekday morning that we cruised into Heathrow's terminal 4. There they were. I had no trouble locating them as they lived up to the image with much credibility. I took the old man's firm hand, but made the mistake of kissing her cheek.

On the ride in the Austin Martin through luscious green fields and red-topped country houses adorned with weather-vanes, the W's (as I came to call them) were quiet at first. The aftermath, no doubt, of my scandalous behaviour at the terminal. Perhaps they even entertained a thought or two of just opening a door and simply leaving me on the road. If they did, it never showed.

"How was your flight, old chap?"

"Good."

"Jolly."

We reached a north-western suburb of London — Maida Vale. Pretty streets, uncommonly regular houses. The Martin pulled into the driveway and we piled out. Mrs. W went straight for the house, and Mr. W and I lugged the single piece of baggage in.

I went up to the attic, which had neatly been converted into a bedroom. It had a skylight, a small bed, a desk, a chest of drawers and little else.

***

"Why are you here, young chappie?" was the first question that greeted me in the morning.

I had gone from old to new overnight.

"To try to write," I stumbled out.

"What do you write?"

"This, that and the other."

"I see."

The marmalade was the kind of stuff friends warn their friends about. Stringy, barky and full of loosely crunching gravel. Mrs. W said not a word, only kept looking at me in a kind of quizzical way. I dropped a fork by mistake but it didn't look much like a mistake, so I didn't bother picking it up.

Mr. W had his routine down pat. Everything was just so. He put on his hat, coat and gloves at precisely the correct moment and made his way out the door, remembering to kiss the wife gently on the left cheek. When she saw me see this, she promptly turned away.

I retreated to the attic, pulled out the old warhorse and began banging away. Nothing at first. Just letters to warm up. A "P", then maybe six "R's" followed by three lines of "Q's". My fingers were stiff and starched and this was the middle of summer. Everything was damp, not wet. The room had this certain mustiness to it; making it a strangely appropriate abode for storytelling. Green lino, bunnies on the wallpaper, a rich amber of a dark wood showing through in places. The rug was an old Persian one, long since clipped of free flight at will. The desk where I sat groaned loudly under the weight, complaining that I should put it through so much and not give it the reward of anything but lines of "Q's" to show for it.

A firm knock on the door. I sat up in surprise. It was her — fingers clasped tightly, almost clutching an invisible rosary. We stared at each other a few long moments.

"What are you writing?"

"A line of 'Q's'."

"I beg your pardon?"

"Just a few 'R's', a 'P' and a couple of lines of 'Q's'."

"Why 'Q'?"

"I don't know. It seemed kind of lonely just stuck up there on the top left all by itself. Nobody pays it much attention. I felt sorry for it."

"I see."

She didn't bother me again that day.

***

Maida Vale sounds nothing like what it is. A very mixed up neighbourhood, I couldn't figure what the Weatherbeaters were doing here. All sense of the pastoral the name might imply was simply an oxymoron. This was a London neighbourhood of no particular identity. Pretty, yet not perfect. Suburban, yet urban enough. In fact, there was something quite mysterious about the whole bloody thing.

I reached the Warwick Avenue tube station and got in for no particular reason other than I tend to be rather subterranean in my preferences. I rode the underground for the better part of the day, comparing Paddington station to Bayswater, Holborn to Aldgate East. I went to all my childhood Monopoly stations and streets — Fenchurch, Kings' Cross, Liverpool, Picadilly Circus. I recalled with some considerable amusement how cheaply I had bought or traded them all.

I went home and had nothing to say, and lesser still to write. I wished to meet no-one, talk to less. I wanted simply to disappear into the fabric of this place, yet I was holding on instead, to sheer muslin cloth, ripping it in my obviousness.

***

I awoke to find an extra "Q" in the list. I know this because it sat alone on a line all by itself, and I would never have subjected it to that.

All through breakfast I was troubled. Mr. and Mrs. W did not say a word. He didn't once look up from the paper to acknowledge my presence. She fidgeted calmly with the cutlery. I remember thinking aloud just how could it be possible for someone to fidget calmly? Yet that was exactly what she was doing.

I went back to my room, taking my Earl-Grey with me. No sooner had the Austin pulled out than the knock repeated itself.

"Did you place that 'Q' on my sheet?"

"No."

"I don't believe you."

"Jolly good. Sit down."

Somewhat nervously, I sat by the edge of the bed.

"What are you writing?"

"Nothing still."

"You can't write about nothing. I have a story I want to tell you."

"I'm sure."

"Sit by the typewriter."

I obeyed calmly.

"How fast do you type?"

"Fast enough."

"I'm going to tell you a story. You're going to write it down."

Before I could interrupt, she had begun.

***

"The alarm by Phaedrus' bed was placed at exactly such a place that when it went off as it always did, at 6:25 a.m., he had merely to drop his right hand off the bed and it would stop. He always slept in the same manner, starched and straight as a lamp-post, with his eyes glued to an invisible spot on the ceiling. On this particular morning, the alarm went off as usual, as did the hand that flew out to meet it. In a moment, his eyes opened as if they had just that moment seen a thing of a shocking nature, but in truth they always opened this way.

He would get up immediately to find his beloved pale-grey bedroom slippers at exactly the same place every morning, by the foot of his bed. It was a mechanical gesture that warranted little thought. The mature bur-gundy-blue silk dressing gown was hung on a wooden hanger by the door of his room. He would carefully remove it, place the hanger back where he found it and then put on the gown. The knot was tied at exactly the same place everyday and the string's fabric was giving way because of his precision. He made a mental note to pick up some more of the material and proceeded out the room.

He would make his way to the bathroom, where his lemon-yellow toothbrush, toothpaste and shaving equip-ment would be neatly placed on a little glass protrusion above the sink, exactly where he had left them the night before. Next to them was the small, white, freshly starched face towel, folded in neat layers. He would go through the motions today as he had yesterday, and all of last week and the week before. When complete, he would put everything back exactly as he found it. The razor went beside the cream, and the toothbrush was rinsed carefully and put back in place. Even the towelette had an engineered niche of its own.

The kitchen was not unlike an army mess. Every item was labelled in neat little glass jars with a certain anonymous capital print that had no particular leaning. All the utensils were in exactly the place he wished them to be, so that even if he were a blind man, he would have been able to do the job with ease.

The electric kettle was tucked away in a left-hand corner, and through its glass veneer he could see that the water level was exactly where it should be, which amounted to just under one cup, leaving a little room for the milk. He would then remove the milk and place it on the kitchen table next to the kettle, so that it might not be too cold when the tea was ready.

He proceeded to remove a cup from its plastic hook off the wall, and followed it with a tea bag, from a long flat glass box in which they were neatly placed like schoolboys in uniform lined up in two neat little rows for roll call. He would diligently lift the first one in line from the left column and replace it with another from the right column.

The sugar always posed a problem, however. The teaspoon that was specially designated to measure the required spoonful, was never accurate enough in its judgements. Often it would be that trifle in excess, and he would tip a little out hoping to level the degree, but more often than not, too much would spill, and as a result, he had to start again and try to get just the right amount. This see-sawing would inevitably continue for a short while until the level of the sugar was absolutely flat, to the point desired. He would then put it in the cup. This exercise, however, almost always unnerved him. He thought it a waste of productive time, and could never get accustomed to the idea that it could not happen at once exactly the way he desired. He had made many mental notes about the matter and tried in vain to find a more accurate method of calculation, but never came up with anything that didn't hint even slightly at the trial-and-error formula which he detested. It never ceased to bother him, though, and this morning, it had done just that.

By exactly this time, however, the whistle would blow and he would switch off the kettle and pour the contents into the cup, where he would let it simmer for precisely two minutes. This was the only trial-and-error experiment that he had liked. He had set aside one week rather grudgingly to time the different formulae and see which suited him the best. It was, however, by the end of the week, a compromise which he had reached. He had found that a three-minute simmer gave his morning cup just the right nuance he wanted, but was appalled at the thought of standing over his cup for three full minutes waiting for it to acquire just the right temperament. No matter how hard he tried to think of what he might have been able to do with those three minutes, it never came to anything substantial. To place everything back as he found it, and replace the exact amount of water in the kettle for the next morning usually took him just under two minutes, and hence the compromise. It was one he was happy to meet.

Cup in hand, he would proceed to the door, where he would find his morning paper. Taking care to carefully lock the door behind him, he would establish himself in his favourite chair, place the cup on a favourite coaster on a coffee table and begin with the papers. Only after he had devoured every word on the front page, would he take the first sip. This ritual was almost holy in its significance.

He was very selective in his reading. He never read the "Letters to the Editor" page, for instance, finding it too trite and unimportant for his liking. He had perused it once and made a mental note never to do so again as he did not wish to partake in the seemingly innocuous problems of the community. He had heard about the "Ask Me" columns in those gossip magazines of dubious repute where seventeen-year-olds would write in saying they were pregnant and needed advice. He likened letters to the editor as much the same.

He never read the sports pages either. He had abhorred the very concept of sport even as a child and never partook in anything even remotely perspirational. He thought it unbecoming to perspire, and moreover, found the very notion of sport an indulgence or a vice he had no need or time for. He could never understand why people and the media gave so much importance to it. He was not against exercise, and took his regular Sunday evening walks, as a gentleman should, but he could never understand two dozen men in obscure attire chasing a piece of pig skin on a grazing field masquerading as sport. He had seen it on the television once, during the six o'clock news, and thereafter made it a point to switch off the set five minutes before the end of the news programme, in order to avoid seeing the sports news.

He didn't bother with the arts or entertainment, either. He never went to the movies, or to a play, and consequently never wanted to know what the people who work in such professions did in their spare time. He found the entertainers only marginally better than the sportsmen. The thought of wasting an evening by the fire with a good book in favour of sitting in an impersonal darkened hall with a thousand others watching an obviously exaggerated state of affairs played out in an improbable scenario was abhorrent. It reeked of a certain hypocrisy and fakeness that he would never accept. He thought the people that worked in such businesses were improper and wished to know nothing about them or the work they did.

Of late, the advertisements had started to bother him as well. He could remember the time when they were confined to certain areas of the newspaper, and even so, were honest and direct in their approach. Now they could be found almost everywhere; on virtually every page, and in virtually every column. Even the front page was not spared eventually, and the conclusion of the lead stories would often be pushed to the back pages. He detested relegating them to such a degree of unimportance that they should be tucked away somewhere between the arts and sports pages, in order to make room for an advertisement.

Even the very top corners of the front page had little messages on them and Phaedrus thought it an outrage that the sacred banner of the paper could be defiled by advertisements for some toilet cleaning liquid or the other. He could not understand it, and when it first happened was almost shocked to the extent that he gave very serious thought to changing papers, but careful research, coupled with the fact that it had been his paper for well over twenty years, grudgingly brought him back to his own. But he never accepted the changes. Even the content of the advertisements had changed dramatically. No longer were the messages direct and honest, instead they were veiled behind some obscure punch line or the other that tried too hard to be original.

His perusal of the newspaper was limited only to the

news. This he found all-important and most gratifying, and he read every bit of it. A news item from even a far off and obscure part of the world was still more significant than the local team winning the district cup in some sport or the other, and certainly a lot more important than the everyday embarrassments in some celebrity's home. The news was what was actually happening in the world, unexaggerated, unbiased and true to life; the basic tenets by which he lived.

The only seemingly ambivalent and incongruous aspect of Phaedrus' well structured life was that every Sunday morning he would also read the comic strips. He could find no justification for it whatsoever, though he tried in vain every Sunday to find one. Finally he settled into another compromise of sorts arguing with his conscience that Sunday was a rest day even in the holy scriptures and that in order to while away an otherwise unproductive day, he would read the funny papers instead, with his second cup of tea; the only luxury he afforded himself. After debating at length the pros and cons of it, he had also come up with the satisfactory conclusion that they were less harmful than either the sports or the arts, as both the situations and characters in the comics were entirely fictional. Come what may, however, on Sundays he would diligently read every strip, including those from across the world. He unwittingly became a devotee of sorts.

Of course, he never laughed or smiled. He just read the comic strips as he would read the news or an obituary. It was part of the Sunday morning ritual, and there was nothing more to it. He did understand all the punchlines, and even appreciated the fine doodlings at times, but he never thought they were there for any purpose, other than the obvious, and that was to merely read them."

***

"I'm tired," I finally volunteer.
"We'll continue tomorrow."

***

This is the English way I remind myself as I run oily
fingers down my pants. The soggy fish-n-chips have
leaked through yesterday's newspaper and the vinegar
smells awful. I sit on steps by Trafalgar Square and look
up at old Nelson on his column, all stiff and upright and
looking rather like he had been wanting to take a crap
all these years and nobody would allow him off the
bloody thing to do so. It's as if all of England wants to
crap real bad, but instead they prefer to keep it in for
decorum and tradition's sake and so, others take the cue
and crap on them instead. Meanwhile, the garbage people
are out on strike as usual, so the whole bloody thing reeks
like .... well, like a nation of people standing in a queue
outside the John, holding it in.

I am about to throw the paper in amongst the seeds
that feed the hungry pigeons. Instead, my eye catches a
flashy column and I deprive myself the pleasure. It is a
strip of cartoons. I go through each, laughing out loud
at the preposterous situations, the weird set-ups, the
gargantuan mistakes, the verbose speeches, the impeccably different sketches of daily life attacked with such
mirth and satire. I fold the paper neatly and place it in
my pocket.

I ponder as to the Weatherbeaters and this mysterious
story-taking on my part. Every night as I retreated to bed,
I would find another "Q" on the sheet, more lonely,

banged down darker than the previous one. Every morning, she would deny having placed it there. Yet, every time the letter would be distant, vague and alone — all sort of violent and misunderstood. Above it, I had my formation of three lines of "Q's" in neat marching order, looking very wholesome and gregarious and happy.

That Sunday morning, I made it a point to serve witness. Mr. W was exactly where I thought he would be, complete with dressing gown, slippers, and his favourite cup of tea. His face was buried in the papers and so I couldn't tell which part he was reading. Mrs. W was pottering with her plants outside in the little semi-urban garden she had managed to manipulate for herself.

"Aren't you curious as to what I'm writing?" I asked.

"I beg your pardon?"

"What I'm writing, Mr. Weatherbeater. Don't you want to know?"

"No. Why would I?"

"I could be blaspheming you. Calling you all sorts of things — names and such."

"Why would you?"

"No particular reason. What time do you get up in the morning Mr. Weatherbeater?"

"Why do you wish to know?"

"No particular reason. I'm just trying to engage you in conversation."

"6.25 a.m. Anything else?"

"No. Not really."

I stare out the window. This has become a mainstream preoccupation in these parts. Staring out the window at a grey and overcast London morning. Mrs. W is fitting the soil around a pot of gardenias. She nudges it, prods it, fixes it again and again until it looks no different than when she started out. Satisfied, and still in her garden gloves, she takes the cloth on which she had been resting her knees off the ground, and neatly folds it two hundred times until it is a small, well-organised bundle. Then she looks all around her to see if anyone is watching. When satisfied that there is nobody about her, she removes her garden shears from their impeccably neat case and shreds the cloth with calm vengeance into tiny little pieces — all of the same size and shape. She places them neatly into a dumpster and makes an imaginary cross and a silent prayer. As she turns, her eyes meet mine. The shears in her hand catch a ray of sunlight and glisten ominously.

***

"Phaedrus was now forty-seven years old. Years, many would argue, that had been spent in a twilight zone of their own mysterious doing. He had no friends, and his few relatives had long since deserted him. To Phaedrus, they were never of any consequence. The few people who had bothered to once talk to him felt more outraged at the loss of not being able to do so, than did he. Certainly nobody ever entered his house, which was his own guarded fortress of sorts. The neighbours talked as always, but even their idle chatter seemed to bother themselves more than it did Phaedrus. However, strangely enough, the curiosity value never diminished at all. If anything, it only grew. Phaedrus was, therefore, the perennial talk show hostage, a sort of unwitting star in his own right.

Phaedrus had worked for the government all of his adult life. It was the only position he held. A disposition many thought most suitable and warranted, and a relationship very germane at best. He was relegated to one of those unspoken and unheard of civil service jobs which were so boring that nobody but Phaedrus could really have done them. Arranging the particulars of the council meeting of the senior citizens of such-and-such place, getting the valid go aheads for the vital task of re-arranging the fiction section in the local library, and matters of such importance. Phaedrus even had a staff of three under him after a devoted and dedicated twenty-six years to the government. These positions were looked upon with much dread among the ranks, and if given the chance, the juniors would pick straws to see who would be sent into banishment.

The truth of the matter, however, was that Phaedrus was a good employer and would never demand more than the necessary. It was just the routine and the boredom of working with such a man that was reprehensible. Even more so was the fact that he looked down upon any signs of mirth or laughter, if ever such dared to arise from those who worked with him.

Phaedrus would walk into his office, exactly on the first stroke of nine, complete with top hat and umbrella, regardless of the day outside. Those in the office often kept time according to him. The first thing he would do was place the umbrella in its stand, and then carefully remove the hat so as not to ruffle even the slightest hair which almost always seemed to be stapled down with a glue so strong that even the roughest of winds would never dislodge it. That done, he would place his briefcase on the table and then walk around it and settle in comfort-ably. His day revolved around the little papers that he would bring into his office, that ordered and structured the remaining hours.

His life in the office was neatly categorised and

governed, moment by precise moment by doing and arranging things of little or no real consequence to anybody but himself. Phaedrus was motivated very keenly by the important and serious nature of the work he did. To him, the rearrangement of the children's fiction section in the local library was as important and difficult a task as the signing of the armistice."

***

"Who is Phaedrus?" I ask.

"A Roman author of verse fables," came the reply.

"No. I mean, who is he really?"

"An Aesop if you will. Told stories through fables."

"What's the shortest distance between two points?" I ask again.

"There is none."

"What do you mean?"

"Precisely that."

"Why are you putting the 'Q's' on my paper?"

"I am not."

***

I slink out into the quiet dark of London. I head for the Maida Vale station and buy a day-pass even though it is already night. I reach Charing Cross, get out, and make my way towards Trafalgar Square. I begin climbing the steep column. I have barely reached anywhere when a Jerry pulls me down.

"What were you trying to do?"

"He needs to take a crap. I was just trying to help him get off."

The nurse wasn't friendly either. I tried explaining the simple logic of my actions, but it didn't wash down as well as the pills that were stuffed down my throat. This is a boiler room. A pressure-cooker stewing well-meaning people. All the windows are locked and bolted down. The ceilings are high, the ground barely rises to meet the feet.

I release myself on my own cognizance and head back home after signing a paper swearing to be responsible for my actions. Everything was very matter-of-fact, pragmatic and to-the-point. After all, it was only every other day that some chap was pulled down the column as he tried to help Nelson get off it to do his thing.

The Weatherbeaters asked what had become of me, over a supper of boiled beans and spuds and light gravy. I narrated the events and they listened courteously and attentively and then went about their work as usual. Mr. W retired to a book of Blake's verses, and Mrs. W went to the sink to wash the dishes. I volunteered my help as I always did, and the offer was once again considered with some incredulity that I should have the gall to so radically request a change in the official programme, and was eventually declined with much formal courtesy.

I retraced myself to my usual spot by the window and watched the rain come down. I counted the particles until infinity and then gave up. Mrs. W went through the motions with an imaginary blindfold on. First the application of the purple-pink latex gloves, the three careful circulations of the generic-brand detergent on the sponge, the first round rinsing, then the washing, then finally, the drying with a fresh cloth. She scrubbed the bottom, the tap, the plate-stand, the counter, going after invisible germs with much menace. When satisfied, she stood by the sink and stared out with me at the light rain as it pattered against the plate glass window. She kept her gloves on. I looked at them uneasily. Moments passed.

A tiny water bug, no more than the size of a fingernail crept cautiously across the kitchen table. I saw it make its tedious progress, but Mrs. W only stared calmly out the window.

"Infinity and one, infinity and two, infinity and three..."

She brought an open palm down against the bug with a ferocity she didn't betray on her face, even as she kept looking out, counting the raindrops. She didn't remove her hand either, instead kept squishing and mashing and pressing against the bug until satisfied that the job had been done properly. Even then, her palm remained on the counter-top a short while, her fingers almost seeming to massage the shiny white formica with an inner glee. Then she turned around and genteelly sauntered off, gloves and all, leaving the bug on its open grave.

***

"It was on one seemingly innocuous Sunday that it happened while Phaedrus was reading the funny papers — never once smiling or acknowledging even slightly, their comic genius.

He always began with Beetle Bailey. This time, the bungling Beetle was arranging his mates for a firing squad rehearsal. He shouted the orders out to everyone and much to Phaedrus's surprise, they all gathered immediately, and took up positions. The guns were pointed out of the paper, and seemed incredibly four dimensional. Bailey was pointing towards Phaedrus and in the next column he shouted "Fire". Before Phaedrus knew it, all hell broke loose.

Suddenly, he was ducking live bullets and Bailey kept shouting "Fire" and they didn't stop firing at Phaedrus.

With complete disbelief, he looked at himself, and he seemed to be bleeding from every conceivable part of his body.

Hagar the Horrible followed next. He was exhorting his Viking comrades to "Charge" and suddenly Phaedrus was thrown back from the chair and onto the ground, as a battering ram kept pounding away at him. Finally, when Phaedrus was pinned to the floor, Hagar grabbed his trusty spear and knifed it through his heart. His ferocious Viking comrades followed suit with their spears and arrows.

Somebody produced a can of spinach and Popeye popped out of his column, swallowed the contents with one big gulp and immediately began pounding Phaedrus' face again and again, with a huge pent up anger.

Even the women and children joined in. Helga emerged from the background and cheered the men on. Popeye's girl friend, Olive, Blondie and friends joined in the cheerleading. Calvin came running from his bed, tightly clutching Hobbes and spouting his usual excitable verbiage volunteering his and Hobbes' services to the crusade. Marvin crawled out from his cot and wailed in excitement. Snoopy jumped down from atop his kennel and egged the men on. Charlie Brown and company wrung Linus' infamous blanket around Phaedrus' neck and squeezed it with joy. From out one sleepy corner, came a big yellow cat with a cheesy grin, begging the men to save Phaedrus for him so that he might stuff him with lasagna and stick him on car windows. Phaedrus was outnumbered."

***

That Sunday morning, Mr. W was in his usual place, with

his usual cup of tea, reading the usual paper. Mrs. W was in her usual place in the garden, once again re-arranging her pot of gardenias. I was watching both from my usual vantage point.

He had just turned the page and arrived at the funny papers when the pot of gardenias came crashing through the plate glass window and struck him at the back of the head.

****

The Marriage of Rita
Marelo

There were only three people in the brass band. The DeSouza brothers were at their off-key best, bulging chests and cheeks into well-polished but out-of-tune instruments. There was the trumpet that played but two discordant notes while Francis dreamed he was Dizzy Gillespie at the Preservation Hall in New Orleans. There was slim Frankie on the Franch Horn — the two had been at the receiving end of several jokes as the horn was bigger than Frankie and he lugged it around like one would a rather obese white elephant. Then there was Faber, the last of the DeSouza brothers, blasting incoherence into an adamantly non-sliding trombone.

Everyone readily agreed that Francis, being the heavy-set one, should have taken up the French horn, and the thin and wiry Frankie, the trumpet. As for Faber, they thought he should have stuck to fishing off Benaulim beach. As marriages went, here in Goa, this was a rather sorry affair.

Not that Rita Marelo cared much for the orchestral maneuverings of the DeSouza brothers, or the low turnout at her wedding in the remote village of Varca in South Goa. Her mind was elsewhere — in the soggy rain-swept streets of south London.

***

They first met at the traditional New Year's Eve Rave off Anjuna beach. He was the typical hippie — long blond matted tresses, torn jammies, earrings, and dirt under uncut finger nails. She was at the counter, one among several other local women, serving cold tea in piping hot dirty glasses.

The first sun of the new year rose from a barren field behind her, illuminating her head completely. For Ed Winters of Brixton, South London, already rather undone by too many amphetamines, it was love at first sight.

Without hesitation, he got down on one knee and recited the complete "Love Song of J. Alfred Prufock" by T. S. Eliot, with a memory and a seriousness of purpose that to this day makes me wince in pain. When he was done with the poem, he proposed to her. She laughed.

***

All of Varca did not turn out for the marriage even though one of their own was tying the knot that day. Xavier DeMello was what Goan mothers affectionately called "a local boy". He was born in a small detached palm-tree lined hut not far from the main church, to a family of rice farmers. He had obtained some obscure art degree from Kala University in Panjim and had hoped to flee the back bending rice-paddy work of planting and harvesting by getting a job in the city that reflected his artistic leanings. But no-one understood what the letters of the degree stood for, least of all Xavier himself, and when two years later, he was still jobless, he consoled himself with the belief that it was because he was over qualified for all the positions to which he had applied.

He had married before — a sweet cherubic Varca girl named Lucy DeMello (not related, being as Goa was then largely populated by DeMellos, DeCostas and DeSouzas). Lucy died within a year of marriage, during childbirth, and everyone thereafter considered Xavier rather unlucky and unwittingly at least, held him somehow responsible for her death.

Now, eight years later, he was marrying again. A woman from the North side, from near Vagator, who had grown up most of her life with those damn hippies.

Rita Marelo closed her eyes as the wedding procession walked down the only main road of Varca towards the gleaming white church. She wanted to trip over something accidentally. But her aging father, knowing her current proclivity, held on firmly to her hand, prepared at all costs to see her through to the altar and then, and not before, to properly give her away to her new life, and her new husband, one he had worked hard to arrange, given the circumstances. And everyone in this neck of Goa would agree to one thing at least — there were several extenuating circumstances regarding the marriage of Rita Marelo.

***

Ed Winters and I had a charmed, albeit brief acquaintance, when he mugged me at knifepoint in broad daylight, one afternoon in Brixton. I was new South of the Thames.

England wasn't cricket and Wimbledon after all. I had been thrown out of my flat-share arrangement at Maida Vale in the North, and was shacking up in an abandoned tenement building not far from Oval station on the northern line. As it turned out, however, Ed Winters was inhabiting the same building I was, and I was soon able to coerce most of my stuff back from him — all it took were reams and reams of poetry; some good, some mediocre, some purely asinine.

Ed Winters had fallen irrevocably attached to the rhyming line, the *italicized* accentuation, the iambic or otherwise pentameter. He never really went to school, according to Ed, and when he accidentally stumbled upon Wordsworth in an until then futile attempt to seduce the love of his life, his skinhead ways began to meander towards the fluff. Soon, he was hooked on all the classical guys with impressive poet-sounding surnames; there was Wordsworth, Longfellow, Keats, Shelley, Eliot and Co. He couldn't read well, Ed, so he had them all read to him, and he diligently memorized everything in between visits to the dole office and the occasional drive-by mugging. He became a literary mercenary, Ed, hanging on each word like a court stenographer with low batteries in her hearing aid. He fancied himself an anarchist, but a poet's anarchist (whatever that implied) although when it came to poetry he would have none of that modern stuff.

"It's not poetry if it don't rhyme and don't mean nothing too, mate," he'd remind me if ever I picked up anything post-1950. He was a purist, Ed was, in matters of love and archaic English set in redundantly passé verse.

It was I who suggested to him that we escape the London winter and head for Goa. "For the cost of a soggy cod and chips wrapped in yesterday's newsprint and sprinkled with last year's vinegar, you can have all the fish curry, local beer and German women with unshaved armpits besides the Arabian Sea." He liked the unshaved armpits bit.

I didn't ever ask Rita Marelo whether she shaved her armpits or not, but I got the impression it didn't exactly matter. Ed the "poet anarchist" was in love with this apparition of beauty, form, function, and simplicity called Rita Marelo, that made all the German women, with their unshaved armpits seem like soggy cod wrapped in yesterday's newsprint. It was love, all right, he confided in me every night as we crashed in our shack at Anjuna beach along with a motley bunch of assorted, accented hippies, sporting ragged Wednesday flea market clothes, and a paperback of the latest American airport-lounge potboiler.

Rita Marelo didn't at first know what to make of Ed Winters. After her immediate laugh, she went about selling her over-priced tea as usual, but Ed Winters just stood there, staring.

"Perhaps she doesn't dig Eliot," he said to me, in a manner close to suicidal, and proceeded to narrate, over the raucous and incessant din of the wordless music, entire passages, ad verbatim, from Longfellow, Keats and the aforementioned Co.

Rita Marelo kept laughing. She was embarrassed in her simple native way at his poetic anarchism coupled with his sincerity. She didn't know what to make of the long tressed Medusa with blonde serpents and earrings where noserings ought to be. She blushed a crimson red, the colour of her skirt, her dark skin all the more incongruous for it. The other girls (whom she thought prettier and far more deserving of his attentions) made certain her embarrassment was not to end by encouraging and spurring him on.

It was midday. Dust clouds from the foot-stomping, raving dancers formed above their heads. Bodies bobbed uncontrollably to unending music. The die-hard acid-goers and colour-droppers were the only ones left, refusing to quit. Ed Winters did not stop gazing at Rita Marelo and many hours after he had begun, and just before he had almost exhausted his hardcover edition of *British Poets, 1750-1950* Rita Marelo figured he wasn't joking after all, and agreed to go to the pictures with him the next day. Her co-workers fixed up all the particulars, and they were to meet outside Vanessa Theater in downtown Calangute to see the Matinee show.

***

The bridesmaids' blue was the Arabian on a cloudless day laced with the white frills of the surf as it crashed against their knees and elbows. They blushed incessantly and giggled furiously until Father Agnello would pierce them with a pedantic look that shut them up quicker than low tide in the dry season. Rita Marelo did not look up. Face down, dry-eyed, unrepentant, she was lightly cajoled across the red carpet towards the altar. Mr. Peter Marelo, in his finest new skin-tight suit from New Lucky Tailors Panjim, (We Cut Closest to the Skin) was not to be denied today. He beamed across at the waiting congregation; he had done it after all. His only daughter, a decent Catholic Goan girl, was, in fact, contrary to local bar-room gossip, marrying a decent local Catholic Goan, and never mind the history.

***

Rita Marelo was not beautiful in the strictest sense of the word — as defined even by good church-going Goan men. She was simply the fisherman's daughter from Vagator, motherless since the age of three, given to understand and appreciate function over form and practicality over beauty. Her hands were the rough of the sea, chafed by tugging too many ropes off wells and boats and lines. Her distended lips, her somewhat narrow and thin eyes, spent gazing at the harsh sun for too many years. Her nimble waist, her simple, (usually red) dress, with the obligatory sash across it. No, Rita Marelo was not beautiful by the everyday acceptance of the limiting meaning of the word.

But Ed Winters' world was limitless, uncharted, undefined, unwritten. For Ed Winters, Rita Marelo was what one would find in the dictionary under "beautiful", and never mind that its meaning had to be read to him first.

"It's this simplicity thing, mate" he kept reiterating to me. "It's this back to basics thing. This is Eve and I'm in her garden of paradise waiting to be offered the fruit."

He waited a long time.

That the matinee show at the Vanessa Theater was *West Side Story* was purely coincidental. Every year the theater owners had to show a smuggled, badly scratched version of the original, or else the local populace would shut the place down in protest. Rita Marelo had seen it just about every year with compunction, but whereas the other Goan girls around her wept bitterly at every scene and dreamed of being whisked away by strong, singing and dancing Anglo-Indian men to Australia or even the Bronx, while their husbands were away rigging oil-wells in the middle-east, Rita Marelo simply watched the film each time as one would a rather somber cartoon.

For Ed Winters, however, everything was symbolic.

The story, the songs, the inter-racial relationship, the coincidence of it all was simply too much to ignore. Rita Marelo was no longer Rita Marelo but a singing, dancing, frock-wearing jewel to fight for — come what may.

Unfortunately for Ed Winters a lot did come his way.

The courtship was furious even if it wasn't fast. "Got to take things at the local pace, mate, got to do it the local way," he'd keep muttering to me, returning as he did most nights at 9 p.m., unkissed, untouched, and hard as Fort Aguada.

This "local pace" and "doing it their way" continued all through the spring and into the summer. To support himself, he got odd-jobs wherever he could — at Tito's on Baga Beach, at the ShoreBar on Anjuna. He started a stall at the Wednesday flea-market and bartered and traded odd-ends furiously. He cut down on Feni and bought his Kerala Grass and Kulu-Manali hashish wholesale and cheap. ("The finest thing you can put in a *chillum* this side of that side, my friend, for you, special price", the dealer had said, and Ed Winters came away with five *tolas* of boot-polish from the back alleys of Bombay.)

Rita Marelo was not unconvinced of his intentions. He told her everything about his street days on the wrong end of London. He showed off a few scars that scared her virgin Mother of Mary soul straight to Bethlehem. She began to feel more and more like a nun at the Church of our Lady of Miracles at Mapusa, where her father took her diligently every Sunday. She felt somehow responsible for Ed Winters, for saving his non-believing Protestant soul and redeeming him in order to obtain the obligatory one-way ticket straight through the pearly gates when God or bad hashish came a-knocking on his door.

If Rita Marelo stood for anything it was pragmatism.

She was as useful with her hands as Ed Winters was with his mind. "You think too much," she would often chastise him kindly, "What's to think so much for?" But Ed Winters could not stop thinking. He was devoutly pursuing the unattainable. He took her everywhere. To Mello's Disco at Calangute (Open Late Nite Every Nite), to Mafia's, the Coconut Inn and to Bob's Inn (where he knew the owners and swore by the curry, and complained about the black exchange rate of the pound being too low), to the Dungeons next to the fort where he tried unsuccessfully again to kiss her, to the backwaters of Goa where no tourist had ever been, to inland beaches, to Divar Island, fishing on the Mandovi, ferries down the Zuari. His Goa was one she didn't even know existed — vast and expansive and unexplored. They watched the sun go down on Canacona Island in the south, they bathed by the waterfalls, and ate prawn *vindaloo* in all the back-alley restaurants of Panjim. Every evening, hand-in-hand, (for that was gradually permitted) they watched the sun set as he recited entire passages in eloquent verse to her.

Rita Marelo did not know she was in love. It was a word uncommon to her pragmatism. If Ed Winters knew only one thing, it was that Rita Marelo was the damnedest thing that had ever happened to him.

***

We were at Calangute, Ed and I, a tip-off we had overheard at Guru Bar in Anjuna by a Yugoslavian with an accent thicker than mortar fire, about an authentic "Manali Man" had brought us here. It was at the Royal Hotel down by the beach. A name so apt for the sprawling white-washed broken down, lino-lined, ill-furnished bunga-low that we shook our heads in earnest approval. Godfrey (not his real name, he assured us) met us in a psychedelic T-shirt and torn underwear, with a hand spread open in greeting more chafed from rubbing leaves together than even Rita Marelo's.

We made small talk. He was a musician, of course, not a dealer. Never done this sort of thing before, ever. Just doing it for friends, to help them out. Who was it that mentioned his name? No-one in particular. Oh, yes, of course, Richie from Bardez, yes, I know him, but then who doesn't? Only for him, I tell you, or else I don't sell this stuff. At cost I give you. Of course, we add, how pleasant of him, and yes, of course, Richie from Bardez and us go back a long way — almost as far back as the Inquisition, I add. Not-his-real-name is now at ease. We're not undercover after all.

Nodding, with an accompanying wink, he retreats inside. Mozart, of all people, is playing on a turntable somewhere. There are paintings on the wall of people drinking the good life, but there is no one in the place, save a few incurious lizards snapping lazy flies. The beach is cluttered with debris to make space junk look like a poor man's wastebasket. Ed starts reciting something by heart, almost to himself, as he drums on the table, and I think it is "To A Skylark" by Shelley, and together with the Mozart I feel like I'm in a lethally subtitled Russian arthouse film where the wind is captured in slow-motion time-lapse to symbolize the working man's "Oh, how blue is thy collar" Blues perhaps. He's thinking of her I can see. Its the wanton lust in his eyes and the sporting bulge in his crotch that gives him away. Shelley is done and away with but Mozart is tripping the light-fantastic as though not-his-real-name had stuffed a sackful of stuff down his throat.

Not-his-real-name returns in a moment with Zabar, an Israeli woman of enchanting beauty, clutching a *chillum* the size of an average Manchester cloth mill's chimney. Zabar, her real name, she enforces, came here when she was but a trifling and got left behind by her hippie parents c/o a Goan family from Cortorim, and grew up thinking she was Goan. The day she was told of her real parentage the shock drove her to clutch firmly onto cloth mill chimneys for the rest of her life from which she spouted voluminous clouds of dense, black non-boot polish smoke provided by her beau-in-arms, not-his-real-name. We smoked a peace pipe, the four of us, and billowed clouds to bring premature winter rain to Goa. Cumulo-nimbus stuff, and not just ordinary wimpy cirrus of the kind you find wafting over less in-the-know *firangi* places. Then we settled down to business.

"This is not just Kulu-Manali stuff my friend," said the not-his-real-name Goan. "It's from Parvati. Even higher. Less spoiled. Less commercial. Just a few spots with some dedicated professional hashishers, not local Himachal *goondas*. And then too — its first flush, you know what that is, no?" We shake our heads in unison. We haven't the bloody foggiest but this is not the time to display naïveté. Zabar blows smoke rings into my face that pregnant circus lions could jump through. I choke, but continue to shake my head gravely and with the serious-ness of purpose the occasion demands. Not-his-real-name proceeds to explain anyway. "Its from the pollen, my friend. Imagine that! From the stamen and the pollen. The best stuff on earth."

As it turned out, we didn't get a chance to test out the best stuff on earth for long, as some decidedly uncooperative undercover local cops barged in at the exact moment that Zabar had strangled my neck with a ring of decidedly vicious intentions. No amount of protestations not-his-real-name offered in Konkani went down well with the undercover gentlemen as he seemed to have a rap sheet the size of her *chillum*, only not so thick. That night, in Ward 2A of the local Panjim police lock-up, the cops confessed they too didn't know not-his-real-name's real name. I was suitably impressed.

When the photograph appeared in the *Navhind Times* ("Goa's first and oldest English language newspaper") the next morning, I couldn't quite help contemplating the redundancy of being both "first" and "oldest". Didn't the former necessarily imply the latter, or had the cloth mill chimney made too many an unforced error towards the general direction of my mouth? While I obsessed on the inanity of the numerous typos and glaring headline space given to "Ferdinand the Cow" who had since the Nylon 6, 6 (a chemical plant) project became operational, only produced a half litre of milk everyday instead of her regular quota of three-quarter litre, the other three so accused with me glared red-eyed and sullenly at the photo. It was taken some time last night with the four of us behind bars and the head of the police department, one Mr. Rodrigues de Fernando Correa DaSilva (his real name I presume, since he wore it proudly on a badge on his lapel where the dyslexic badge writer apportioned too much space for the first few names only to subsequently cram the last two words back-to-back in infinitesimally small type) posing smugly in a firm handshake with the Chief Minister, who's name was not as alluring or challenging to remember. That was us, all right. No denying it. Zabar was still firmly clutching her chimney as though it was her life-support system, and not-his-real-name's underwear looked decidedly garish, what with the stripes and dots and smudges and tears in appropriate places. I thought I looked all right, even though I had red-eye from an ancient flash. But Ed Winters was sweating like a responsible porcupine trapped in a condom factory in an overpopulated third world country, trying to find his way out without exploding the birth rate.

He had been here before, of course, in the best jails that London could offer, but this time was different, because all he could think of was her. He'd promised not to touch the stuff, apparently, and had even sworn allegiance to the Lady of Miracles, in Mapusa, genuflecting on sore knees, right hand on his heart on his right hand on his heart, no less.

The bail was posted within a few days, wired via the Barclays Bank in Hampstead, through the account of Mr. and Mrs. Winters of 24 South Hampton Road, and routed via the Canara Bank of Panjim, Goa headquarters. We were both out within five weeks of incarceration, passports and papers impounded, trial to be conducted four months and some weeks hence at the High Court next to the Secretariat in downtown Panjim.

***

Ed Winters headed straight for Vagator to track down the Marelo family. He did know where exactly she lived for she had never let him take her home after a date. At the end of the day, some inquisitive neighbours, hungry and eager for gossip, who wanted to know what a punk kid from London had in common with Peter the fisherman's daughter, showed him the way to the Marelo residence.

Mr. Peter Marelo was first introduced to Ed Winters by Ed Winters himself.

"Yes she is fine, thank you. Just gone off on her honeymoon. She was married last night you see... and your name is...?"

"Ed. Ed Winters. Has she... has she... she... last night?"

"Yes."

"Has she not mentioned me... to you?"

"No. Why do you ask?"

"She's never mentioned me to you in all these months?"

"No. Why should she?"

Ed Winters did not ponder the question. He left the village promptly and headed back to Anjuna. That night he burned all his poetry books — the anthologies, the collections, everything. We sat by the bonfire on the beach, Ed and I, as I failed to stop him. He was not despondent, he was not despairing. It was a simple measure — an exacting, well-thought out one.

Then he dropped four large squares of acid, howled at the moon and flung himself into the deep black of the sea.

***

When Peter Marelo read Goa's "oldest and first" and found out about Ed Winters, an indecent Protestant punk kid from London, his old heart sprang into renewed action, and although all of North Goa seemed to know of their "unholy" liaison, Peter Marelo managed to find and convince Xavier DeMello from the small and distant town of Varca in the South, that marrying his daughter would be a second coming for him.

And so it came to pass, on what seemed like the last hurrah of the monsoon and the last night of our incarceration, before I skipped the light-fandango on a cargo ship to a newer never-never land, the marriage of Rita

Marelo took place in a rather somber, low-key manner.

****

Brothers in the Know

Say it ain't so brother, say it ain't.

But no this shit really happened brother, take it from me, it did.

There this bar in Amsterdam you see we shagged once upon a longish time back. There I was at the entrance, stand and all, selling my half weed and pips and all at discount rock shit bottom prices and you walked on by and I saw in a flash that it was time for your fix. Your legs gave it aways you see, and I could tell by the way yer head lolled to and fro like a slow train to nowhere that it had been a while brother, a while my brother, I know, I know. I too been there before. Fugdatshit and let me take you inside where you can thaw them balls out.

The Rembrandt bar in Rembrandt place in the heart of do-goody canal-land a stone throw from the red light area and I might as well have Anne Frank under me table blowing me off for all I care. This is picture-postcard material. You know my brother — the sorta shit that gets a dumped to mean as average Joe Nobody relatives in Toledo and places that don't warrant a mention in a map with a magnifying glass. The sort of postcard that says been there done that and what are you up to these days, Joe my brother?

Ah but its warm.

From freezing sleet and snow and cold and inside there's that thing like hard as raw gin and gripped close to the heart my brother, it warms the cuckolds and neanderthal regions. Sit, sit yer shags down. This my place.

I bring out the selection.

Grass from Kerala, the finest. Hashish — you want Afghan, Kulu, what? Just speak my friend and its yours. All soft, no damage it done nobody and legal too. What? No coke and no powders neither. Don't do that stuff my friend, no good for you. Hardens the arteries and what good all the highs in the world with hardened arteries, I say?

So I sees this man rollin' out clutching them ribs and spitting them spit a mile to never-never land and I says to myself, I says, whatgood this stuff if a man not even good 'nough to even hold his dickie up heavenwards, like true men, I say? He's got this trail of piss yellow as a dog's frozen come on stale newspaper and no respect neither. No respect neither I say, my friend. You as junkie and so ok.

I move on.

There are bars many and places to do things that rest of world says no to. I gotta life. I got customers I gotta job. They say it legal and shit to sell but hey no bringing the shit in that no good. That illegal. Go figure yourself into hairy knot, ya know, what I care? These rules maken't a pig's head sense in a pork eating world. Sell them OK, importing them no OK. So how I do business? You tell me? How the shit land here in the first place you tell me my friend? DHL? No. Man called big ugly motherfucker from bad part of world come to doorstep and dark as shit he dumps crateloads onto me to piss on. What I do brother but sell the stuff? Its legal and I a good businessman.

I know from where you sit this looky a bit wonky-tonk, yes? But no.

This shit good, I know.

So I walk down cycle paths and bump onto two-wheelers and cuss my lungs out as I go to new pastures. There is the Jimi Hendrix bar and the Reggae place and there are the night shenans and what have you.

I know this place love, come with me.

It called iT with a small i and big T, exactly as I spell it and man, is it happenin' or what?

You know you do good when you got buskers seven feet tall and as many round, black as sin and shit combined. I mean raw as dogs fuckin' and getting stuck. You know what I mean? You see it some times when they're at it and like crazy glue or somethin' it over and nowhere to go but staystuck ass-to-ass like bumper to bumper traffic on a highway for rest of their friggin' lives. They mean brother. Take it from me. I was a dog once. I found out my pastlife transgressions, (that big word I know) from Madam Zelda opposite the *Central Station* in downtown side. But where *was* I ? Oh yes, mean as fuck and I known what I mean man when I say mean.

So the iT it is, and ask no questions. This place cool as a cucumber up a ladies' you know what. Dudes and dudesses and tresses long and matted blond to waist and the muzak, what to say?

What to say? Except too funky. Down and out consciousness raisin' shit. New age, jazz, techno, rap, acid, funk, groove, house, cart, lock stock and shit loada barrels swingin' tonight man and I make my rounds and this what I say.

Yo and a yo and yer pretty folks out here a groovin' hear me and I tell you no lies man I got shit to snort and snuff to shit and everything that goes in between and I tell you man ain't a nigger this side of that side save the fuckin' mother continent can get you shit purer than mine like treacle down a honeycomb, like a baby's behind, I mean smooth so smooth you'll wanna maybe slide the raft, shoot the falls, skip the planet, you know what I mean, brother?

And maybe I shove some and maybe I snuff out competition becoz I blacker than the blackest crack of yer ass where the sun don't shine notime, you know what I mean? And I do good. Gooder than Santa on Christmas Eve I drop goodies down chimneys so large I go back for reinforcements and mostly its the women man whiter than pale snow, like cocaine on velvet snuffed by golden cigarette holders and they dig me man, they do I know.

Like the otherday for instance.

I was a selling at another fav jaunt you know — the old and trusty RoXY, yer spell it jus like I did there — RoXY, you no ask why the shit so fancy with small and cap letters but its free world, at least when you're damned in Amsterdamn and no fuck gonna tell yer otherwise.

So there I was at RoXY yer know and she comes upto me in them dark as dungeon with the lights gone out corner they have and grabs me crotch like it were a bowling ball or raw damn tangerine tryin' to ripe it faster than fast. And I wanna scream but hey, I a man, and a black man, so no good that sissy stuff. Meanwhile I turn a zillion shades of pinky even for a black motherfucker like me but she just hold on like a vice with a screw too tight maybe.

Then she drops a number into my ear whispered like black pearls from the French Pacific and goes to loo out.

So like a dog in heat ain't got too much since last mating season I lap behind her and tongue hangin' to Antarctica for all I care and I sees that she ... with another woman, whiter and paler than original sin and all they want from me is some good shit to go down nice and cheap and easy you know? And hey ... under normal circumstances, being the businessman and all improving Dutch foreign relations and adding to the national bounty and I a decent tax-evading citizen of the first world, maybe I say no, this shit too deep and dark and silk to come smooth as free, you know?

But I hard as the Pontiff under his garb grabbing his sceptre and what have you and maybe the good lord will hear me out this one at confession then may be again... not.

So its the RoXY and the iT and the new dang fashioned high tech, gizmo shita happenin' thing called the Chemistry bar and I can a tell you even a motherfucker like me who been seen all damn places in town in this here part of the world ain't seen nothin' yet till I try my biology at the Chemistry bar. This shit too hot to burn your fingers as I write and you read maybe some other time when we better acquainted, yes?

Mean a while I frequent the night life. Only here in Amsterdam I tell you, you can shop for yer pussy like it were toaster ovens. And what frequency, and what model and does it plug into sockets in Greece and what have you and what after sales and pre tax and post service can I expect and oh yes of course, do you dig the plastic, man?

Today's special? Buy one get one half price ... Even a businessman like me tell you ... that good marketing. Glass cages, like a modern shopping mall and pussies to make your eye sore to pick and choose like in them supermarkets thing walk down like stag in locked horns and they a starin' at you from ground floor and walk ups all in cleaner glass than a boudoir I know on the east side. So you point and choose and haggle and maybe they say ok. But mostly ... at 200 guilders a pop, I say fuckit. The pop ain't a popping enough you know what I mean? Makes no business sense I say.

And then there are the tourists. Damn fuckin' tourists may the sweet lord bless them a plenty. Whiter and paler than the law should allow they sweep down tight crotchety and ain't a lay since Oxford beat Cambridge in the boat regatta. I seen them eyes I tell you. Hungry as hyenas after a fuck, only not so content.

Them northern types. Europeans with funny money and thicker accents than my brothers in the islands would permit. But see its this free capitalism thing — you want, you get and fuck there ain't no place on earth like this place to get what wants when and how and why you ask no questions I no tell you no lies...

Ok brother?

I can tell yell you ... I been there, I done that ... I seen shit you won't believe...

And then it happened...

There I was as easy as going it ever gets black man

with a hard on and an honest job doing my thing, makin' the rounds, know what I mean and I meet this dude one day right outta palookaville and he just took shit and made shinola outta it man, and I ain't kiddin' neither.

Like it was that I was outside the National Museum no don't know why so don't ask me and I see this dude with happenin' dreads and a fake wannabe Rasta accent from fuck knows which third world country and he comes up and buys the shit cool as he been born here, and good stuff too with no hagglin' like them eurofreaks. So I curious to know more... we go to tram ride I think it was number 24 to nowhere.

Yes I know now. That it all right.

And he get talkin' about this and that and what else have you and I got a listenin' and he says he something like a part time writer and full time bum and I a listenin' like it were OK you know no hot flashes and no revelations either but I can't figure what the fuck he is and where the fuck he from you know what I mean brother?

He ain't no brother o' mine but he got attitude.

He ain't blacker than an Ethiopian long distance runner but he got shades you know?

Sure he can swag and walk but him accent kinda confused you know? Look something like a third world reject trying to pass off as a Brother and not doing too bad neither.

So OK. I mean big fuck I care. He buy my stuff I listen...

He say he come here to find Vincent. Half the land is fuckin' with the Vincent name brother, where you been?

But no... our dude after Van Gogh himself... the original thing.

Now I ain't much of a learner and can't say I sat in class a minute longer than piles could afford but I know this dude Vincent buried longer than a hard on could stay in a group of oil-wrestling Scandinavian women, you know what I mean brother?

So I tell him so. And he says, this what he says, and I quote as he says what he says coz yer gotta hear it to believe it that...

"The man lives in his work..." and I says I says to him yeah so do I only no body none the ever frame me like shit and hang me from nails on walls for strangers to snap at.

And so here we are... at the Van Gogh museum and I think this guy a bit too soft for me you know? I mean who buy good shit from Laos and Cambodia and them fancy places with oriental names in a place like this? Might as well throw a rave in the library, know what I mean?

He pays the fuckin' fare I tell you. I feel I like at pearly gates to heaven and there ain't no mean as prize-cock bouncers here with a hangover neither.

Hey, St. Peter wait up... I a comin... only not so fast.

So ok. I dig. The guy a genius ok?

Not the dude tourist with a funny accent jerk. The dude Vincent whatsisname.

But no flashes neither and me dick ain't even hard yet...

But then it happened...

There were four of them... in a row neatly like an execution a waitin' to happen and a gang a people rapin' them with them eyes. Like I mean rape you have to see to believe... these four a them I tell you... four shits to change your life. Can't say I know what it was really, coz I'll a be bull-shitting in a cowshed you know, and that ain't right. Nor it ain't legal I know.

But there was something there.

Cornfields, chapel at night, simple shit but the more you look at 'em, hey, I swear by my purest Afghan shit that the Ayatollah could give me, this was mean and serious man... and I know I was a doomed.

So OK. What was it you ask?

I dunno. Just stood there like a mummified jerk in a nerd line-up and stared like a never not even for the dudesses at the RoXY stared like my eyeballs would pop and shout stop, you know what I mean brother?

Anyone who done this... could do anythin'.

And maybe that was all there was to it brother, you know what I mean?

And so then I turn reformed man I tell you. I shat the shit, didn't even bother the sale and said to myself I said — whattis you really wanna do brother?

Fuck if I know came the reply.

And I tell you this. I'm still fucked.

I try and try to get the goddamn shit outta my head but hey...

How can he do that shit and expect normal to remain so?

I was fucked in me head for longer than I remember. Then I went back... so OK ... this here is Amsterdam. The most beautiful city in the world and ain't no place more shag to smoke in and more shyster to get yer laid in. But hey... I got them medicine for the blues... the shit comes from Afghania and Mongolia and China and India and places you wouldn't dip yer dick into for catching the plague... but I get 'em here for you. pure as shit on snow.

And things I tell yer... went back as they were and I wuz a motherfucker with a neat clean and decent hard on all over again.

(The lord hath mercy...)

***

Fat Aunts and Goannas

There is a woman outside of my window flashing her breasts. I can tell from my vantage position that they are rather large, of the kind that has to constantly deny the urge to simply fall from the tree, like Newton's apple.

Today is my birthday, my eighteenth, I am told. Inside, the party is raging unabated. Curry permeates the air in a thick nauseating fog. Fat aunts hover over the kitchen table, concealing layers of duplicitous skin like stripped bacon in a bun. Forehead polka dotted, fingers ringed in carats unfathomable. Their greased skins are sweaty with the burden of oil and vanishing lotions and get-fair-quick promises. They poke about what was once my kitchen. It is swarming with enough obnoxious half-breeds as to warrant a drastic change in immigration policies. They raid the food with a mission; salt-free, low cholesterol chips washed down with a two-litre of Diet Coke.

Right now, however, it is her with the large breasts,
that has my undivided attention. It is not that I do not
know her. It's just that at this thorny junction, I wish that
she would simply heave her buns somehow over her
shoulder and march off into her waiting car. I can hear
the engine purring softly. An import with a fancy label.
I see the pair of dice hanging ever so quaintly from the
rear-view mirror, and the barking spotted dog at the back,
yapping at imaginary traffic behind.

She is waving now. Her breasts sway and flow like
oil on water. She is yelling threatening words I try
desperately to lip-read. She stops a moment. Then starts
to undo the rest. The zip cuts through my mind like a
cat's whisker on milk. The laces undo themselves in so
much of a hurry as to have a will of their own. I run
out in a frenzy. She stops. She looks at me quizzically,
with the sort of innocence that inquires as to what I was
doing on my lawn, while she was minding her own
business?

"G'Day" she says, in that self-deprecating Aussie
manner that always suggests a question mark — "Nice
party".

Her pants are at her feet, fallen in that urgent sort of
manner that implies a lot more than if they were off
completely. Her breasts, now denied the motion, sag like
a willow on a low river in the dry season. Her head is
cocked to one side, in that "Who me?" gesture. She knew
all right. She had me by my short and curlies, and was
lapping it up, savouring the moment for posterity. I had
to invite her in now — I was left with no choice.

"Er... hullo," I say, with the deepest sort of accent I
can conjure up at a moment's notice — "This here is
Bernadette".

That was a mistake — the jargon too colloquial. The fat lady in the rayon sari reaches a limp hand out. The movement I see, is recorded in the eyes, the statement is burrowed in the eyebrows. "G'Day". This from Bernadette. The two shake hands like adversaries at a United Nations meeting here to decide unilateral arms reduction. Of course, the Indian lady keeps pumping her hand up and down vigorously, in the official manner of greeting the foreigner in her own land. Bernadette tries to free herself, but is taken with same hand and led into the kitchen.

The silence cuts through the curry with a jagged knife of the sort seen in army-supply stores. They stare at her, making the hardest possible effort pretending not to. Every sari is a bright red with horns. We make the obligatory rounds. Bernadette keeps trying to out-guess me on my parents. I won't give her the satisfaction, hoping she trips up at the right moment.

I should have known better, I tell myself. Women have antennae when it comes to such things. Mom stopped just short of telling her the secret bank account number, and her now immortalised recipe for *dhansak* on Sunday afternoons.

"I tell you Berny, the way to a man's wallet is always through his stomach. The more you feed him after all, the more he has to loosen his belt!"

My mother of eighteen years is another person suddenly. These are words I have never heard. They scrimmage through her closets and cupboards and other "secret" places I will likely never see. They giggle away in the sort of manner that puts to shame centuries of differences in culture and language and funny accents. I realise very quickly that with a mutual enemy in mind, a woman could liaise effortlessly with another, agreeing

on common ground faster than they can reach it. Soon
my baby pictures are out, and the embarrassed squeals
get louder and more hysterical. I know when I've lost the
battle. I withdraw discreetly.

***

The black Holden pick-up with the dark curtains pulls into
the parking lot at Bondi beach. Probationary license plates
hang from front and back, loudly bemoaning their "P"
status as a dire warning of sorts to fellow drivers. She
rolls her pane down half way, and pushes the rest down
with the palms of both her hands. Her golden locks fall
about the side of the battered ute; caressing them, teasing
them. Her eyes are blue as the Pacific on a clear day, the
clouds vanishing into them, trapped in a state of perpetual
limbo. She smiles. The freckles are pushed outward, the
mandatory Australian wrinkles around the eyes from
being out in the sun too long, are further accentuated.

"Berny", as I have come to call her of late, is stretched
out across mother's Indian cotton towel — pale and white
across a blond sand. I can see the family initials at one
corner, inscribed in fancy red thread, stitched on years ago
by some servant in Bombay. I nonchalantly throw the
suntan over it. She is reading a play by David Williamson,
the local playwright, "stretching her horizons", she informs me. I bury myself into the final chapters of *Tropic
of Cancer*, a cheap unabridged paperback version I stole
at the Paddington Flea market last weekend. I can see from
the corner of my eye, that she is hardly reading. One eye
fritters about the beach, the other is glazed by the water,
and somehow, by osmosis, perhaps, she is taking it all in.
I do not think she knows Henry Miller and I am not about
to explain him, nor the book, for that matter. I wonder

myself what he's doing lost in Dijon, wrapped in mustard, as I lie here burning my own crumpets to a crisp.

Babloo is upon me. He is in his well-pressed and pleated trousers, of course, with moccasins or pull-ons or whatever you call them in your part of the world. The type that has those three little strings with fancy knots on the end hanging just above where the toes ought to be. His starched shirt looks as though a boat-fuil of illegal Chinese immigrant dry-cleaners in Haymarket went to work on it. The shades are pure Manly Promenade stuff. Five dollars with a little haggling off an old Italian man from Parramatta Road in Leichardt. They have green neon arms and lenses so thick and black, they're almost camouflaged by his skin.

"Hullo *yaar*, what are you doing here today, eh?" He gives me the authentic Indian wink, the imaginary nudge and the raised right eyebrow. This is followed by the disguised sneer of contempt, which always manages to imply horrendous implications only fellow brethren (however removed) can adequately translate.

The girl raises her head at him now, then looks at me, expecting an explanation. I shrug.

"I'm living the Australian dream," I say, "How about you?"

"Me?"

"Yes you, Babloo. You. What are you doing here? In this place? At Bondi?"

"Oh nothing *yaar*. Nothing. Just taking a walk. Maybe buy some Yeeros or Doners or doing something like that while I wait for the Misses to come home. Nothing really. *Yaar*, just a walk. My SAAB is parked just beyond over there".

"Is the remote on?"

"Of course *yaar*. What you thinking? You not thinking I don't know where I am ?"

I do believe I don't think he knows where he is, but I let it pass.

"You wanting to hear it? Ha? What say? You wanting I press the remote?"

"That would be neat, thanks, mate."

He flips out the little black thing from his pocket which is attached to his trouser loophole by one of those archaic accommodations with more chains than sense. He tosses it in his hands in the manner of his favourite South Indian star, and presses the button. Two quick beeps a hundred yards away. He winks and smiles his crooked white teeth at me. I am stunned at how white they are.

"Great. Did you pay the attendant at the south side as you entered?"

"Entered? For what?" He is shocked.

"For parking. You mean you didn't pay?"

"Where? I didn't see no one."

"You didn't do a good job Babloo. They'll tow your bloody SAAB away before you can get there in your fancy bloody shoes with the three little bells."

He looks down at them, a paler shade of black. The tips of his ears are red and glowing like the neon in his shades. I miss the smile. Now he's a round black patch against a brilliant Bondi sky. He darts away, kicking sand everywhere.

"Hey, watch it mate," — usually the extent of the vocabulary in these parts.

He boulders over the low wall, steeple-chasing his way to his beloved SAAB with the fancy remote and personalised license plate that reads "BABLOO".

"You know there's no attendant, and no parking fee,"

she informs me.

"No!" I say, with the sort of belied innocence that warrants a couple of accents over the word. "No worries, he'll probably pay the life guard anyway".

The girl in the black ute walks up to me. Her shadow falls across my groin. She is topless, and wears just enough to remain legal downstairs, though I doubt that very much too. She bites her lip, in the sort of manner hazardous to men with weak bladders. I can hear a grumbling in my stomach. Miller has been put to bed. She tosses her head sideways, and runs off into the water, gyrating to maximum possible effect. Berny is staring at me point-blank. Even through her shades I can see her pupils dilate, but with just a touch of arsenic. I ignore her and return to Miller. I pick up the book upside down. I know I am not very convincing right now, considering the implications of this act, which are not lost on her.

"Tropic of Capricorn already? You're a fast reader, I must say."

I turn the book around. Australians are not altogether insular, I remind myself.

***

Personally, I do not like socials. A "social" for the uninitiated, is the equivalent of the high school prom night. In Australia it is best described as the only valid excuse throughout the year for teenagers without licenses to borrow their parents' cars and get totally smashed in a twenty dollar rented tux. The sending of the tux to the dry-cleaner in the morning before returning it to the rental shop is a custom passed down through the generations and adhered to as strictly as Anzac Day.

I do not like socials, primarily because this is already

my fourth one this season, and my first season to boot. The socials season usually starts in November. Summer has parked herself on the backyard right beside the Hills Hoist and the esky of Fosters. Lunacy is everywhere. The neighbours you haven't seen in months are swarmed by every kid on the street, ploughing in their pool. There is smoke every evening from every patio, pool-side and lawn. There are no shrimps, but sausages, and steaks are frying feverishly in the Bar-B-Q's. A man stands beside it, thong-clad, singlet-ed, Fosters in one hand, pliers in the other, as he turns the sausage over with the air of a three-star Michelin chef. It is the loony season all right.

There are too many unwritten rules about this annual do. It is the mating ritual that few pass, the driver's test into manhood. Those that do pass, join the ranks of men, the rest are left behind in some primordial womb of their own reckoning. You do not drink Fosters. You drink Victoria Bitter if you're from Sydney proper, and XXXX Castlemaine if you're not. You do not bring your sister to the social, and try and play down the similarity in features. You do not dance the fox-trot. In fact the less you dance, the more perceivably "cool" you are, and logically, therefore, "hot" property. This is a silent auction. The men leave early, right after dinner, slightly off their equilibrium, carried off discreetly by the women. The boys stay back and talk about Aussie rules and how the Swans suck, and why Balmain, not Manly, was the greatest League team ever built. The girls are too busy hoping nobody sees their zits to pay any attention. I have been to flea markets, and then some ...

It was Berny's idea. We went to the same night class together at the Hornsby Tech. on the North Shore. This was the post-HSC bash, and I could hardly refuse. At the

dinner table, a round white-linened, candlelit arrangement, four couples were seated, in their year's best finery.
Every eye had the sort of look that tried in vain to disguise
the goings-on under the immaculate table-cloth. Often,
legs and hands would get confused, with the boys usually
making the most of the occasion. Berny is watching me
watch the girl in the black ute from the beach. Berny
fidgets with her cocktail — twirling her olive, stuck to
a pink umbrella made in Taiwan. The girl in the ute is
across the table, her legs all over mine. I had no idea we
were in the same school. Her boyfriend is a dressed-up
Westie from out Penrith way perhaps. The sort more at
home in the usual red-checked woollen shirt every outback
town hangs to dry from its back yards. Tonight, he is in
a tux, with the tie loose in the sort of very calculated
manner of looking casual that took hours to prepare and
perfect. His hair hangs over his forehead in dirty locks.
A Winfield stub is perched precariously from one corner
of his mouth, as though by the skin of his teeth. Berny
is, to put it mildly, not entirely pleased.

"G'Day mate, I'm Adam, what's your name?" the
Westie asks, surprisingly articulate.

I spell it out slowly in my usual manner. He sits up
attentively.

"Do you always have to spell your name out?"

"Always."

"Why".

"Because people like you would never understand
otherwise."

"I understand." He tries it once. I shake my head. He
tries it again. I shake it once more.

"Why the fuck is it so complicated?"

"It's not."

The girl in the black ute pipes in. "I think it's cute."

She has the sort of voice you hear in commercials for lingerie.

"I beg your pardon?" I repeat, the excuse presenting itself.

"You don't have to beg her pardon just because you didn't hear her!" Berny chimes in as diplomatically as possible.

"It's just a figure of speech." I'm coming to my own defence rather too quickly, I know. "I'm going to call you Kev," the Westie speaks.

"Thanks Anil" I retort.

The man is momentarily stunned. Is he a good Christian or what?

"Me name's Adam," he yells, spelling it for me benefit, "A-D-A-M".

"I know Anil." I find myself retorting. The Victoria Bitter has gone to me head.

Silence. Berny has swallowed her olive. It is an unpleasant experience. She does not like olives, least of all when she swallows them by mistake. She had explicitly asked the waiter not to put an olive in her drink, but he thought he heard otherwise. The girl in the black ute is slipping lower in her chair. She bites her lip again in that manner I said before that drives men prematurely to the John, weak bladder or not. Anil is furious, his bow-tie has lost its casual edge and is now buried almost completely by his collar and jacket. The Winfield almost burns down to the filter before he puts it out. Berny is grappling with the long-legged misses from the black ute. A shoe falls, and by the sound of it I can tell it's a stiletto. Another abrupt silence. The black ute stares wistfully at me. Berny drops her fork in the time-honoured manner that says

"Oops! Clumsy me! I dropped my fork by mistake!" and bends down to pick it up. I know it is not her shoe, and that she only wants evidence in the matter.

It is nice being of exotic descent, I remind myself. Kind of like being the only iguana in a zoo full of goannas.

***

The fat aunt is in her usual backless zebra-striped, off-the-shoulder, almost above-the-waist costume. It is clear that her knees and elbows have spent the better part of their lives facing the brutal Indian summer. They are wrinkled like a long-dried prune, darkened like the native, thin and scraggly.

The tandoori is dipped in so much low-fat yoghurt as to warrant a recipe of its own. The chutney is mild and watered down. I am elbow deep in the red of the tandoori paste, licking it off grateful fingers. There is a fight beside the TV set. The Melbournians want to watch Fitzroy tackle Carlton, Sydneysiders outnumber them, so we settle for a boring round between St. George and Wests. The Fosters flows freely — the novice women all have a touch too much lemonade in it, to make just the perfect shandy for this balmy Sydney afternoon. I am scouting for bones to chew, dogs to harass, bottle caps to pry open with teeth, used condoms to throw into the pool, nieces and nephews to annoy, married women to make love to. I am unsuccessful in all but the last.

There is a room in the basement, lit only by a naked bulb, hanging limply by the thread of its own will. It is a dark and musty room, littered with old furniture, broken toys, phonograph records, and other scraps to a collective archaic memorabilia. There is a bed. A makeshift sort that rattles and creaks its arthritic limbs under the weight of fat aunts wearing Kanjeevaram saris too thick and ornery to acquiesce easily.

A hurried whisper, an unzipping, a struggle with complicated bra tacks and chunky jewellery and hastened by temporary fleeting guilt, we make love. A sort of fly-by-night love. A quicker-than-thou shooting star in a galaxy of brightly burning hits and misses and glances furtive and tempestuous. Smudged lipstick tucked into its proper corners by yellow-laced doilies and bed sheets. A pressing of the sari by hand, a creasing of wrinkles, a quick check in mirrors of compacts. A few fleeting seconds to smoothen hair, touch up mascara, peer through a crack in the door, and finally, a re-entry into sanctimonious worlds and boring husbands.

This time, however, a bump into another patient in the ante-room of life's secrets. A gasp, followed by quick remorseless guilt, coupled eventually with the knowing nod of co-conspirators after a shared bounty. A lowered gaze, then a prompt two-step back into respectability, via a quick shot on the rocks at the bar.

***

It is the harsh glare of late January. The red has climbed to over thirty degrees in the shade, and sunscreens have given way to sun blocks. Sweaty beads dance the salsa across my forehead, often doing the tango to a merrily confused waltz in three steps, one inebriated. The Coke can is shot through with heady brown stuff from out of the drive-by liquor store. The beach is a haze under mirages. Bronzed bodies, golden locks, surf-suits, parasols wilting under the noon day sun.

This is how it has been. All the way from Surfers Paradise in Queensland to Airlie beach to Great Keppel

Island in the Whitsundays. The Barrier Reef has me intoxicated with colour and light enough to want to come back in next lives, perhaps as one of those inedible fish that swim in the waters. Miles here are measured in kilometres, which are measured in six-packs of Castlemaine XXXX. So far, we have travelled twenty-four six-packs, and are parched dry as the land around us.

Berny and I have no particular destination in mind. The roads have wound their way past back-alleys and dirt paths and outback homes with front yards the size of Tokyo. Roads even a mother couldn't love. The beat-up Toyota station wagon, sky-blue as a cloudless day in January, is packed brown with permanent layers of rust and dust and the dry workings of a cruel land. Every so often, the lure of sand and surf drags us back, steering-wheel eastward-bound to stretches of virgin dunes. We go to places with names that would make Wagga Wagga and Woy Woy look demure.

We have transported ourselves forty thousand years into time, and forty years backwards into progress, and the original tenants of these withered rocks and sun-burned lands are now homeless. This aboriginal town is but a blunt mile long, frayed at the edges. Tin shacks with moth-eaten blankets for doors. A 1957 Holden pick-up with no license plates. Rusted through and through. A makeshift hills-hoist of wood and lumber, creaks its way into a still breeze. White shirts hang with the dread of time and oppression, stained permanently by both. Heads are held low, eyes averted. Groups coalesce in corners. Little girls with ponytails. Young men clutching half-empty bottles, caressing the touch like that of a lover, living between fortnightly dole checks, meted out with substantial guilt and rote, by governments in Canberra.

Mothers cooking in open earth furnaces, stirring Goanna and brewing ransoms to good health. Old men on their haunches, gossiping lazy afternoons away. The town is weighed down by anchors white and rotten. The flesh of the ship, like that of an empty hull eking eons away on a permanent low-tide.

Towns with no names, towns with thirteen letter alliterated names that tie tongues like two contortionists French kissing. Berny drives past them, complexion changing, eyes glued to roads too narrow to avoid the abundant display of grief and poverty.

We do not talk. Thoughts are transmuted somehow, across the great vast divide that separates us. She, in search of adventure. Me, in search of self. Our only meeting ground is the search itself. Our destinations, like our origins, too different to warrant comparisons. I have seen worse in my own land, yet there I have had few yardsticks with which to measure grief, save more grief itself. Somehow, blackened, hardened skins have little use for the pleasures of sand and sun. There's far too much history to swallow first, like bitter pills, to allow leisure to spoil the fun. Berny, she tells me, belongs to the guilt of her peoples time, one that she bears not so lightly.

***

On the beach again. We buy a T-shirt that says we got wrecked at Great Keppel — the best place in the world to get wrecked. We go boom-net riding and para-sailing and wind surfing and snorkelling and scuba diving. We while away lazy hours and endless nights reading existential angst and the impossibility of the id. We count stars, measure waves, number particles of sand and give them names.

We are a strange sight. Wherever we go, there are curious eyebrows raised. I flaunt it, revel in it, thrive on it. She knows this. I am the prize bull in an exquisite China shop, and pointed looks pierce like ignorant arrows from immature, insular matadors. They retard damage like zinc on the nose blocks the sun. Berny is not as comfortable in my wet suit as I am. I am comfortable in most suits, worn or unworn, fake or genuine, leather-clad or silk-bound, khadi or khaki, naked or adorned with the plumage of pomp and circumstance. I am always in front of one of those trick mirrors at the neighbourhood amusement park, where multiple images spring forth.

The trip ended before it could really get anywhere. There was no destination. We stopped only when we ran out of gas and went back home. Via different routes.

***

The girl from the black ute is outside of my window throwing stones. And shoes. And rocks. Her blonde hair falls about her supple shoulders and seems to caress them in ample folds. Even though I can't hear what she's saying, I can make out the swear words by reading her lips. They are short and unintelligent. A stiletto comes crashing through the window, sending shards flying across the room. I duck nonchalantly. I saw it coming.

The party comes to an abrupt halt. A shriek or two, but no more. A sudden silent pause to yawn by. I turn around and head for my birthday cake. Nineteen candles. How the year has passed, how little of the ritual has changed. Bushy eyebrows and oily hair nod their together-ness in my general direction, awaiting explanations. I wash the cake down with Victoria Bitter and a leg of juicy tandoori.

I recognise faces from past encounters. Babloo is here, this time with four little bells on his shoes, just above where his toes ought to be. All my fat aunts are here. In freshly pressed leopard-skins and Kanjeevarams. I identify past loves, past couch-trips, back-seats, telephone booths and glass elevators in crowded shopping malls. All of them now have their righteous insignia sharpened, ready to point fingers and set loose wagging tongues too long untied. Another shoe breaks forth and I watch it sail in all its slow-motion glory as it weakly cracks its vengeance across another window.

I go out slowly. Eyes are burning holes into my back. "G'Day" she says, in that self-deprecating Aussie manner that always suggests a question mark — "Nice party".

I take her by the hand and lead her in. "This is Camilla," I say to all and sundry.

"G'Day", she snaps back with the open friendliness of the land.

Something tells me I have been here before.

****

Baguettes, Red Wine and
Men's Haircuts

$\mathcal{I}$t was difficult respecting Louisa in the morning.

I strike up the coal-oven furnace and place the blackened pot over the red amber, with brown water to boil for morning coffee. I light the Gitane with a hot coal held in a drooping wet towel and feel it singe the cotton. I stare coldly at the tiny freckles of fire as it dances its way skywards.

We were on the Place de la Bastille, where the fourth arrondissement meets the twelfth, the eleventh and almost the third. That Parisian district where history seems to have been written on every wall and facade, and where, with a little imagination, one can almost see the ramparts and scrape blood off the once cobbled streets. Outside of my window I can see the Colonne de Juillet, rising its pomposity into a grey sky, proclaiming its inherent right to hold the keys to all virtuosity, for here indeed, as history will prove, all equality was born. At the far end, a sight one can only see in modern Paris, is the new Opera Bastille; an exercise in ugliness, a protruding tongue at lifetimes spent in the creation of the aesthetic. A gargantuan cement and steel and window monstrosity that is almost an April fool's joke in a cold and bitter January.

Louisa stirs. She is naked, of course. A thin, torn and browning sheet caresses her lazily, folding over her creases. I watch her sleep. She is too perfect, even as perfection goes, and hence my inability to respect her in the morning. Nimble shoulders, apple-tart breasts, black eyes, ruby red lips that seem to bleed their redness dry. She begs a canvas, pleads a frame, lures an artist insane. I think of the futility of the man before his palette and paint as he tries to capture her. He must necessarily give up the pursuit. I think of the inadequacy of the writer to find words enough. He must tear at his hair in frustration. Louisa was too perfect to love her.

It is a rancorous morning. Bitter as medicine. The wind is merciless against pale flesh, as it pulls it asunder. The cheap jacket bought with an hours' worth of sleazy bargaining is no match for this viciousness. I pull up the flaps against my ears and head down the street. Looking up, I can see it is Beaumarchais. All Parisian streets look ridiculously alike, far too pretty to be real. The only way I can tell them apart, even though I walk them endlessly every day, is by reading the label. The Boulevard Beaumarchais. Very well, if you say so. It might as well be Saint Michel, Fauborg or the Quai d'Orsay to me.

I am not headed anywhere except wherever this chap Beaumarchais has not taken me before. I am in search of something tangible, except I do not know what it is. I know that I must be able to see it, and touch it, and believe it for real. It cannot be perfect as everything around me has become. This museum piece. I know only that I am seeking a certain imperfection, a certain vulnerability, a certain state of being not so carved in stone and placed on a pedestal as to be unable to realise it for real. That is my goal today, as it has been for many long months in this city.

Near the Place des Vosges I stop in one of those little Jewish tea houses and drink jasmine from an ornate vase with a spout. It is scalding. I have to lacquer my tongue with saliva to keep it from hissing. A black tunic and skull cap with curls down the side sits next to me. He looks me up and down awaiting explanations I haven't the wherewithal to give. He is a curious fellow, eyes all beat up and screwy from probing other people's business.

"What are you searching for?"

"I do not know."

"You do not know?"

"No."

"There must be something specific you want?"

"Yes."

"What?"

"Another jasmine tea."

"What else?"

"I don't know yet, but when I see it, I'll know what it is."

"How long have you been searching?"

"As long as I remember."

"Can I help?"

"Yes. Get me another tea. Not so hot this time. I'm running out of saliva."

"Eighteen francs."

"Now I remember what I'm searching for."

"What?"

"Precisely eighteen francs. I don't have it."

"I thought so. When you find whatever you're looking for, let me know. We'll have another tea."

"I will. *Au revoir.*"

"*Au revoir.*"

This is how it has been. Chance fleeting encounters like passages from the bible of avant-gardism. I recall Brecht and Joyce, Bresson and Sartre, and can now understand why the narrative story is so passé here. Even ordinary meetings become extraordinarily exceptional. It's like all Paris views life with a different pair of glasses from the rest of the world — always slightly out of focus.

***

I cut through to the rue Saint Paul and head for the left bank and the Latin quarter. I walk across the Ile Saint Louis and no sooner than I hit the Boulevard Saint Germain, I am affronted by civilisation and all its chaos. People. Everywhere. Mink coats and fur underbellies. Faces brutal against the harsh wind, eyes screwed up all tiny and minuscule. Papier-mâché people. Bending with the wind. Stilletos and poodles with matching fur. Cigarette holders caressed in exquisitely slender fingers. The accent is suddenly thicker and more lugubrious. I reach the Sorbonne.

Outside, students in berets and paper-thin notebooks laze in the first break of a mild sun. A flashlight sun that radiates only light. The Gauloises are out, the conversation is animated and boisterous. I hear translations, French to English via Greek via the classics. I hear arguments, Becket versus Camus. Manet and Monet. Hands are everywhere, radiating the rib cage perilously close to people and

things, they dart in and out like an old cartoon, unsophisti-
cated to new technology.

I reach Saint Germain des Pres and go into its heavy
laden halls and thick carved pews. At the far end, a
minister in garb is pulling away at the last smoke from
a cigarette, clutched firmly between thumb and middle
finger. A bevy of beautiful nuns strut the pews like it were
centre stage on the Moulin Rouge, handing out satchels
of instant forgiveness for the price of a few francs. On
the last pew a couple is making out. He has her skirt hiked
up to her waist, and only his bare bottom rises and falls
like the inflections of every carol and psalm. How nice
of Him to provide satin knee-rests, however faded they
might be.

Outside, the sun is even brighter. I squint just a little,
allowing a slow window into first light. I am lost even
for a man who has nowhere to go. I sit on one of those
naked benches by the street and complete the picture
postcard. I am a tourist attraction. Come feed me crumbs
and I'll pose for the polaroid.

***

Night descends without premonition. A sudden blanket-
ing darkness that obliterates last light. I have wound my
way back through the masses, artificially huddled together
in a consentual warmth, towards the Seine and the Notre
Dame. I am in the heart of it all. Kilometre Zero. I climb
the graffiti-ridden stairwell of the Notre Dame and esca-
late slowly towards the roof, expecting at any corner to
bump into Quasimodo. But here, instead, Bertrand met
Isabelle. Here still Jean-Pierre came in '84. Vincent loves
Clara but she loves Jean-Francois. The etchings and
ramblings of unrepentant love are scrambled everywhere.

Much women's gold and ornaments and jewellery went into the ash heap of history to build this temple to the stained glass, but Vincent is only enamoured by Clara who has other things on her mind to care about the ornaments of time and aesthetics.

I reach the top and look out across the Latin quarter, over the Left Bank, and see for once why Paris is Paris, spring time or not. There is much madness in the air, much hysteria, much love, much sorrow, much pain, much anxiety, much sympathy. There is much of everything. It is infected with humanity. A large, over-abundant humanity that accepts even if it never understands. An invigorating, phantasmagoric humanity hanging across every clothes line, dancing over every rooftop, making love on every park bench and pew.

I look below and see a tiny sign obscured by cafes and street signs and crumbling wall facades. *Shakespeare & Co.* In Paris? Intrigued, I lower myself once more into the echelons of this humanity and cross the Seine into the little book shop. Immediately I am lost.

The yellowed-dust of cruel time, the sagging weight of falling book shelves. The haphazard cartons piled ceiling high with books, the makeshift tables. The narrow passage, the gentle murmurings, the coffee stains and ringlets from old cups. The smoke-infested atmosphere, the clouds of vapour hanging to every escape for dear life. The little aphorisms carved into wood spoken by everyone from Durrell to Miller, from Joyce to Oates. It is a veritable amusement park of the mind, a roller coaster ride to abrupt orgasm.

I work my way to the back. A poetry reading is in session, or so I think. Twenty or so Parisians are huddled together on the floor, on ladders, on makeshift tables and chairs. Some sit atop books, those pretentious with prolific prose enough to warrant the odd posse or pantheon of derrières. An old man fronts the mike and is explaining in grungy detail the multiple and myriad joys of the fart, canonising its music to new realms. Another tells of the proper etiquette of picking one's nose in public, rhymed in French no less, in iambic pentameter and complete with hubris and hamartia. The real spectacle I think is in the audience. With a dead earnest seriousness of purpose, heads bob to and fro, in agreement, or in the occasional display of being distraught, yet nondescriptly nonplussed. I sigh in relief and exgurgitate myself, stomping my way to another level.

I am upstairs now. More books as wall-paper. More cobwebs. More dog ears than on all the dogs of Paris. I close my eyes and thimble through dusty jackets, making a clean streak down lapels, wanting to stop at just the right one. Imagining what it would be. With my luck, an atlas perhaps, with places new and virgin and not yet feasted upon. I stop with brevity and foresight on a small volume. It is Henry Miller. *Quiet Days in Clichy.* How germane. How typical of me to pick that one even in my slumberous stupor of a blinded sleep.

***

Louisa and I argue over oysters and a cheap Saint Laurant Classic red baring its soul with a *Grand Vin Sec*, not even the ho-hum template of a *Vin de Pays*. It is adulterated fruit juice made up in a chemistry laboratory in some peasant town flat as my tongue on a non-ulcerous day, only not as interesting. We argue about the quiet days Miller spent in Clichy. She feels cheated by the latter-day realisation that his memoirs were largely fictional even in the use of the first person. Imagination, I plead, is the only individualism left. Whether he did what he said he did is hardly relevant to the way he says he did what he did. I am tripping over semantics. She swallows a shell, doesn't bother to try to get it out, only lifts the empty plate and smashes it against the wall.

"It was empty," she says, in defence unrequited.

***

Someday I'll write my own memoirs too. Perhaps I'll call it *Quiet Days in Bastille*. Things are too good with Louisa. I want to paint her, garnish her, adorn her. One cannot make love to a deity, and if one does, how can one respect it in the morning? Perfection unbecomes a good sex life. I am still searching. I realise my journey has defaulted into the destination itself.

***

I am speaking French in subtitles. Tired of it all. The greyness of the sky, the pale skeletal trees with scattered branches fighting the cold draft, the mothers with strollers, the cobbled courtyards, the naked benches, the decadent statues, the entire ebb and flow of humanity as it crushes past me. It is altogether too perfect, this mosaic.

I hurry into a neighbourhood *tabac*. It is getting late. Outside I can see the first lamps light up. It is a corner store of sorts, grown permanently into a withered pavement. A few French papers, yellowed pages testament to old news, a rusting chair or two, a table with three legs, one short. I order the usual baguette, scrimmage for loose change and slap it on the counter. I think I imagined it, but I believe the man smiled. Surely not in Paris? I wonder aloud if the cold is taking its toll. I look again — closer.

Under that bristling moustache of the gendarme of a previous century, he is smiling, if only just.

"*Ca va?*"

"*Oui, Ca va*"

"*Francais?*"

That was it, of course. He could tell I was somewhat new, an alien perhaps, exotica of some sort, no doubt. Perhaps he could learn a foreign word or two to impress the mistress into cunnilingus unimagined. But the question is asked, nevertheless, and as I have ample times before, I stumble for an answer.

"No. No." I say, hands out and protruding. "*Je ne suis pas Francais,*" hoping he'll leave it at that. But no, I get the friendliest *tabac* owner in all of Paris on just the day I'd rather not talk. I fumble in torn pockets and soles of shoes and inside compartments I never knew existed as I place centime after centime before him. He looks at me with some bemusement. I have barely reached a Franc or thereabouts and have run out of more exeats to hunger. He looks down at the counter a fraction of a moment, then back up at me. We both know I am not even close. I shrug callously. He opens a palm and frisks the little pieces of silver into a drawer. Then he turns and finds, with some caution and discrepancy, the finest loaf of a baguette there is. Big and burly and crisp and loaded with sesame and other such shenanigans. He places it on the counter in front of me. I cannot reach for it somehow. The distance is too close to permit.

"Only if you tell me where you are from." This in a poor man's English.

"Why?"

"Because."

"Because what?"

"Because. That's why. Because. There is no other answer. I have no reason to know. No need to know. It won't change my life in any great way. I just want to know, and since you're getting this for nothing, that's the least you can do."

He has a certain point. I look down at the bread. So close, so inviting. I can smell its dough rise in such aromatic pirouettes as to make thieves of honest men. I look back at him. It is not an unfair or unusual request. It is just that I am unable to answer him for reasons I cannot understand. Where am I from? How many times have I heard that before? Where am I from? Physically, metaphorically, geographically? Which answer does he seek with such vicious blackmail? What bribe do I have to offer?

I search my pockets again. Every nook and corner and niche and alcove and fold and lapel. Not a sou. I'd rather pay this man a king's ransom right now than answer that question. I do not know why. I have nothing to hide from him, nothing to add, nothing to take away. I do not fear the label, nor the parameters of the ubiquitous box, the glass ceiling, the mirror on the wall. I do not fear the prejudice of time or place or race or class or caste or every which permutation therein. I do not care for the raised eyebrow, the nod of approval, the hiss of dissent, the withdrawal of insularity or ignorance, or both. Yet I am unable to respond to that question, even if its rhetoric is innocuous, its answer obvious. I realise suddenly it is the *necessity* of asking that question itself that rankles me the most. Where am I from?

"Of no fixed address," I finally state, as I take the baguette and head for a table.

I sit at one end of the tiny *tabac* and dig into the

baguette with the glee of a prospector striking gold after years spent tearing up empty earth. I wipe numb fingers down my pants to keep them warm. I cup both hands and blow into them. The baguette is crisp and fresh and tender. I savour it in minuscule morsels like the manna from gods too penurious of late.

A small glass of red wine is gingerly placed on my table. I hold it by the base, clasped like a clothes-pin by thumb and forefinger, and bring it to the nose. I swivel it a little and notice the heavy legs run down the side. Strong. Full bodied. I hold it up against the dirty white table cloth and am reassured by its opaqueness. Dense. I swivel some more, then check the bouquet. Heady. Aromatic. I sample it, rinsing clear to and fro, rolling it on my tongue. Then I spit it out.

"Chateau Latour, Cabernet Sauvignon, 1983."

"Bordeaux 1961," came the terse reply.

I swallow. My face red as the wine. I look up. He is not affronted. The moustache bristles with imaginary pique. He is smiling. I have no doubt about it now. He is smiling. I have gone almost a year in this place without seeing that. I realise how wondrous it is that this man can smile, that it is possible even in this town, and especially in light of what just happened.

"*Oui monsieur.* Bordeaux '61".

I begin to protest. Arms flailing impeccably, head shaking involuntarily. I want to get down on my knees and lick the ground where I spat it out. He sits down. I stare at him.

How can this be, I ask? He pulls out the bottle. I read the label.

Chateau Petrus
100% Merlot

Appellation Pomerol Controlee
Bordeaux 1961.
Maybe I have reached the end of my search. Maybe.

***

"There are only three things in Paris the French government subsidises. Do you know what they are?"

I shake the head sideways, affirming the negative. He opens the cork gently, as though prying a stubborn baby out of its mother's womb. He pours himself a quarter glass. It is many minutes later that he takes his first swill, glorious in all its manifestations. He is making love now. The foreplay took three decades and more. A tiny dew drop coagulates at the tip of his tongue which he rolls inwards with the penchant of a man who knows how to treat ambrosia when given it.

"What are the three most important things, monsieur, that man cannot, simply cannot live without?" And with this statement, he emphatically banged an open fist on the table, ensuring beforehand, that both glasses and the bottle were removed. My baguette almost rolled off the table, on account of its scurvy or polio, I know not which.

"Three most important things?"

"*Oui monsieur!*"

"I do not know."

"Baguettes, red wine and men's haircuts."

***

This room. This tiny room on a fifth floor walk up Bastille Armageddon. Smoking Gitanes lit by old stoves too dreary to alight to new passions. Asking rhetorical questions, finding redundant answers, when all the real solutions lay in subsidising baguettes, red wine and men's haircuts.

How simplistic, how brilliantly conceived this notion. It didn't matter that Louisa had told me this was hardly true. The French are notorious for subsidising everything. But if men could have cheap wine, bread and haircuts, what else could they possibly want?

I flick tobacco from my tongue from off filterless blunts and pick at it like lentil seeds on cotton balls. There are shapely clouds of cigarette smoke that choke for want of an escape, forming alphabets and sentences, complete with grammar and punctuation. There is an old turntable continuously playing one obscure tune in a beggar's parochial French. I sit on the floor, back against the wall and face the cold impersonality of the Remington type-writer, stolen by Louisa for me two days earlier at a Montmartre fleamarket. There is a single paper in it. I have already used one side and for lack of the sou, hope to use the other, marginless, ribbon faded into some perma-nent illegibility.

I am thinking of Louisa. We met at the Jardin Du Luxembourg last spring, when the love nests were warm with groping hands. We were sitting at opposite ends of the same bench, all infinity between us trapped in the space of a thimble. She opened *"l'Etranger"* by Camus to page one or one hundred, I do not know, and began reading with the sort of immersion that belies any move-ment in the stratosphere. I opened *"The Stranger"* by Camus and read the subtitle, from page one or page one hundred, I do not know.

With every page that passed the thimble diminished its scope for the carriage of much space. No one sat between us. People stood and talked, leaned against trees and talked, sat on cold cobble and talked. No one chose to sit on our bench. We never looked up at each other, not even for the momentary recognition of each others' presence. We were fatalists — believers of some Byzantine symbolism perhaps.

The sun dipped into quartiers alien and Latin. Stars sprung from shadowy corners. The moon, a half-faced jovial pock-marked clown, jumped out at us from behind man's clumsy concrete attempts to reach it. We read on in partial darkness until I do not remember how long. I remember only that we finished together, closing books in sporadic sighs of helplessness coupled with an existential id.

"Let's go home."

I do not remember who spoke, nor does it matter in the general scheme of things. We have had little necessity for the spoken word since, talking instead, in glaring subtext translated in the fine invisible ink of nuance.

I remove the sheet for I have run out of space. I flip it over and can hardly read what went before. Still, I go searching for more paper, only to find nothing, not even the scraps of notebooks or address pads or the back of cigarette boxes or the rolls of toilet-paper. It is useless. This story, like so many others before, will remain unfinished.

I sit by the cold cavernous fireplace and stare at its numbing belly. I crush the single sheet with unrepentant vengeance and feed its hunger. I light the stove, find a flame to carry and set fire to my words. I watch them dance and flare up and rise joyously into freedom. At least they serve me warmth if nothing else, even if only momentary. I need an escape from this perfection, mired as I am in images of struggling Parisian writers starving themselves to sleep.

Yet, it is true. I am hungry. I take Louisa's wide shawl and wrap it tightly against my stomach, knotting it just above the navel. It is an old hunger-staving technique I learned many years earlier and have since had to utilise on several occasions. To divert the mind off empty stomachs, I tease a blade into a bulbous vein. Its sharp edge pierces brittle skin like Moses unto the Red Sea and I begin my own mass movements. Tiny rivulets at first spring forth to new life and drip down towards my elbows only to merge pell-mell with the doings of other slashings. I am playing naughts and crosses with my mind now as I draw lines horizontal and vertical, making the acute observation of how much more the latter tells as it pops veins down the sieve. Two lines, this way and that, and soon I begin with a cross in the centre square. A tiny insertion no more than a miniature Christ. I know the game's outcome already — it is prewarned towards a draw. That is its natural inclination as it always has been.

Still I plunder on, savaging all god's good intentions, playing my own lord and surgeon with steady hands. A naught here, a cross there, another naught. The turning of the blade in a confined circle within a box is limiting, tauntingly difficult. The pain is already past me. I am licking the juices up my arm like a pig after a truffle. There is almost a pleasure now — numbingly beautiful, a sort of drive-by poetry. Church bells and peeling laughter. I am hungry again now as I lick and clean myself like a mother feline would her new-born.

The sheets are thick and soiled through and through like a flimsy diaper on a stubborn child. It coagulates into shapes of countries and places and faces. It coerces memories long since left unremembered, of escapes and chases and runnings-away and more escapes, from people and events and things and what not. I stick a finger in the mess and create my own past. I obliterate faces and white out others. I crease and caress the stains and tempt them into words and letters for want of space on which to write. The temporary relief tempts the opening of more sluices.

Louisa enters. She sits by the bed and scruffles my hair, entangling her fingers. She turns my wrists upwards and gently kisses the throbbing veins, inducing incentives too dangerous. She wraps the sheets around them gently, places my head on her lap and begins to sing a proletarian song, or melody I think, in French. A sort of bathroom meets the lounge voice. Even in my weak French I could tell it had something to do with the poor striking miners in Emile Zola's book, or perhaps a verse or two from Moliere or Proust. I was slowly losing consciousness and her French was too thick and fast to decipher. I remember mostly the elegiac, lyrical voice with which she sung. I remember thinking too just before I passed out that the sheets needed changing.

***

The face is blurred and I cannot see who it is, but soon the vision clears and I see it is her with an expression of pain and worry writ large across her forehead. The robes they have outfitted me in are starched so tight I feel like I am in a strait jacket. I laugh at the thought until I look around me and the walls have suddenly disappeared and the floor is upon them and the carpet is too thick and I think I'm too weak to have woken so soon. But the walls are actually the way they are, only they are padded today and slowly the realisation dawns upon me.

I have been here before, but today is different. There is an air of quiet solitude about me hanging like the pall over a dead body. Louisa stares that vacant stare of hers, still looking too cheerful to make sense. She knows I haven't the answer she is searching for, and nor do I know anymore what the question is. But her hand is in mine all right and there is a strange sort of redemption in the feeling, like that of the executioner shaking hands with the one to be executed before she commits the deed. I try to raise my hands a little, and I see they're wrapped in enough white as to cover a dozen corpses, yet the red is still seeping through the layers. The smell is putrid and the stench of yesterdays everything envelopes the room like a stale hangover.

***

The door creaked open and an overweight nurse walked into the room. Louisa exchanged conspiratorial glances with the woman; murmurings in the foreign tongue of concealment. Then she turned around to look at me as if for one last time, before squeezing my hand tight and getting up to leave. The fat woman leaned her onion breath into me and whispered sweet nothings in Gallic or Gaelic for all I remember. Suddenly the door opened again and four strapping youths paraded in like police-men on their rounds, and before I knew it, my hands and legs were pinned down by a force so great I thought they would snap in pieces.

The woman leaned over me again and brushed her wide and spatial breasts against my face, in a smothering too affected to be real. Then she tied a cloth over my eyes and my body was already shaking. Soon, I was screaming once more a scream I had become familiar with of late. More men came into the room and pinned me down. The force was so brutal I was sure I would break in two like a piece of candy in the hands of a starving mob gone mad.

Cold metal cuffs were tied to my ankles and to my hands
and little metal pads were placed over my head and across
every conceivable naked part of me. I was left there,
crucified to a bed, deceived by my very own, and sold
for nothing, not even the kiss of mortality, nor for thirty
rotten pieces of silver. And then it happened.

What felt like a thousand volts ran up my spine and
down again and up again and down to the ends of my
feet and up to the edges of my consciousness. I was being
electrocuted like a mosquito in an electric cell of contain-
ment and every nerve fibre in my body was alive to the
feeling, akin to being struck by lightning again and again
in the dead of day.

***

Three months and more removed and we are in the
darkened hall of a typically small Parisian cinema. The
screen is lit up with images in shoddy black and white.
High-grain, fuzzy with the passage of nitrous time,
inflammable liquids and sunny shelves in long-lost film
libraries. There is no story here, just the image. I realise
it is a contemporary piece, scratched and plagiarised and
cheated into all history. What an illusion, I think aloud,
that everyone here thinks it was made in a distant past.
I sit mesmerised nevertheless until Louisa's hand gently
reaches out and touches mine.

I scream. Again. And again and again and again, until
at least two turn around to complain. Then, in my best
starched-collar French I berate the audience for being too
wrapped up in each other and not the movie.

They turn, of course, back to the screen and the usher
comes out of a shadowy abyss, pants almost to his ankles,
and with great dismay at being stopped short of his

plundering ways, manages to throw us out with some grace and aplomb, all things considered.

***

I am fast awake by the foreplay of dawn. It teases me, caresses me and promises me pleasures all delivered if only I awoke from my rigid stupor and embraced the day. I turn to Louisa and look at her for what I think will be the last time. I ponder as to her gentle dreams and muse over them. She is in sleep so content, her smile is too wide, too innocent. I wonder too often what she is doing here with me. She will not leave, I know, whatever I say or do or protest. I must needs out again.

I slip into the quasi-darkness of early Paris. The grey brick walls everywhere still have lengthy shadows and the streets are shimmering with dew and frostbite. This time I know where I'm headed. My route is fixed. There is no struggle.

I walk from arondissement to arondissement, from quartier to quartier, stumbling over drunks and beggars, bypassing traps and promises, avoiding bookstores and landmarks and *tabacs*, neglecting street signs and diversions. I head from one end of my life to the other; crossing mental roadblocks, checking references, annulling promises, withstanding lures and bribes and destinations new. I walk with a sense of purpose I have not known for a long time. I am propelled, as if by remote control, following some inner order of things, not as they ought to be, but finally as they really are.

I take in every little detail. The stereo sound of the priest as he makes his sermon from inside the *sacre couer* on surround sound Dolby. The circus outside. The trapeze act from building to building. The artist's canvas and palette and the face before, replicated in exacting detail, and for a few francs more, without the wrinkles. I walk down the much-photographed steps to *Pigalle* and watch the neon and the hustle and bustle of early shoppers of flesh after a night gone terribly lonely. I sneak into a Metro, awaiting doors to open for me from other sides, by kind, fare-paying Parisians. I regale myself with the eclectic inanities of the panhandlers, professors and puritans alike. Before me, a man possessing the saddest pair of eyes I have ever seen gets up with a totter and delivers a passionate sermon on *liberte, egalite, fraternite*. His breath is sour sans the sou, foul with alcohol and love lost, equally bitter with both. I get off at my planned destination. How strange I think it is to arrive exactly where I set out to be.

I go into the *tabac*. The man has clearly been expecting me. We stare at each other a long moment, reading the others' thoughts. I take out my life-savings and place it carefully before him.

"Baguette. Red wine."

He brings both, and takes the money without counting it. He flips it into an empty drawer.

"Which way?" I ask.

I take the baguette and the bottle and follow his directions until I reach the nearby saloon.

"A haircut, please," I state.

"Subsidised".

*****

Anytown, USA

The fruit was plastic. And enormous.

The suits were starched until necks lay trapped guillotine-like, pin-striped, buttoned down, and tethered by tie clips and cuffs and other such anchorage. The three men had a desperate air of casualness about them that belied their worried looks as they sat across at the far end of the table. Their breathing came as hard as mine, as though we were all in a sauna room. One even had his sleeves somewhat rolled up, in that lets-get-to-work manner, but the folds were too careful and calculated, creased down by the weight of many well-meaning irons.

At the other end, was my agent, Morris Will, or something to that effect. Morris was old establishment Hollywood. Third generation string-puller, gave nepotism its notoriety as the family kept the job in the blood. He is casually calculated today. Leaning back somewhat, fingers pressed together at the tips, bald spot glistening under artificial sun, a loose cashmere giving away his afternoon plans at the golf range.

There is a silence in the room and I know Morris has created it. It is one of his induced-for-temporary-effect silences. The breathing is heavy, punch-laden. I cannot help but stare at the enormous bowl of fruit slap-bang at the centre of the table. Plastic as plaster of Paris, only not as edible.

"Think Lawrence of Arabia on a passage to India to find the jewel in the crown."

I know Morris said those words, for they came from his general direction, but I still look for the hidden microphone somewhere up his sleeve. But no, they are his all right, and the suits are nodding excitedly now, all bobbing together. They resemble a row of gaudy clowns at the circus, with wide open mouths into which hapless men attempt to feed ping-pong balls to impress the girl by winning a cheap teddy from Taiwan. The air is suddenly thick and heavy, enough to cut with the blunt and unwitting edge of a fourth draft screenplay. They turn to me, expecting words of wisdom, affirmations, nods and meaningful aphorisms. I reach for a large and shiny red apple, complete with plastic stamen and single leaf and place it in my torn pocket.

"I'm hungry," I state in that matter-of-fact manner, as I turn and leave the room.

***

The car park is big as the Goofy enclosure at Disneyland in Anaheim, only the name tags sport Ebenezer and Donald Duck. The glistening manifestations of shining automobiles baring far-too-cute license plates is not lost on me. The Range Rovers are out in force too, complete with car phones and tinted windows. I go to the far end and slip my battered keys into my faithful '79 Chevy. I ease in uncomfortably, the heat having taken its toll on steering wheel and seat alike. I roll the window down and breathe. Deeply. I can almost see the smog as it enters my mouth. I feel like an intruder with night vision capable of seeing thin air, the kind one sees every week in those movies of the month. As the engine slowly purrs to life, KISS FM blares its white music into numb ears for want of anything better to hear. I ease past the reserved parking lots and the chrome and metal of Benzs and Royces, attempting nicks here and there, until finally I slip into Beverly Boulevard.

I cut south from La Brea until I reach the Santa Monica Freeway 10. I have crossed dangerous rivers and rapids, I have swum in wide oceans flat and far as the eye can see, I have climbed mountains in the Himalayas, I have faced the wrong side of a .22 as I stumbled into a political coup, I have traversed through Tundra and Sahara alike, I have even faced the Motor Vehicle Department staff in countries that invented the word bureaucracy, but nothing has ever tested me as much as westbound on Freeway 10 at rush hour. Nothing. I understand now why some go off the far end and whip out pistols and the like and spray all and sundry with a mind gone frustratingly mad at 5 m.p.h. I stick my head out for some relief, only to choke from a hostile mouth-to-mouth resuscitation by smog-emitting mufflers. I see the speed limit sign of 55 and laugh till I reach near-hysteria. This is a child's prank, I think aloud. A Halloween trick or treat, in poor taste. Give me a two-year old with an axe through her skull anyday.

An hour later I make my turn south on the 405 and head home to Long Beach. Another hour later, and I have reached at last. Sweaty and tired with the peregrinations of the day, I flop onto the floor and stare impassionedly at the ceiling.

There is an arrhythmic thumping, a sort of hit and slap on flesh and bone, followed by a falling of utensils and a clash of furniture. A short cry. Piercing. The irregularity of the movements, the occasionally audible swearing, and the femininity of the anguished sobs and shrieks deliver its truth too plainly to ignore. I am tired. I shut my eyes and try to close out the sound without much luck. I stare at the massive blobs of black jelly on the ceiling — the desecrations of time, cigarette smoke, fungi and poor cement. The noise does not go away, only becomes more sporadic in its viciousness. Every so often it is punctuated by a gun shot or two from down the block.

I knock on the nameless door. No reply. I knock again, only louder. A long moment of hesitation for strangers are doubly strange in these parts when they pay house calls. A crack in the door. A large metal home-grown chain fastened to concrete allows only the width of presumed security to wander in. He is large and obese with his girth trapped under a soiled vest, unable to hold much more weight. His scruffy beard is entangled in itself, red and stained with spilled beer and mis-spat tobacco. His eyes are narrow and deep set with unmitigated loathe. I do not recognize the .38 in his hand by the label. Decidedly a foreign import.

"Yeah?"

"I'm trying to stare at my ceiling without getting disturbed. Do you mind?"

"You some kinda wacko or what?"

"Can you try and beat her up when I'm not home please?"

"It disturbs you, huh?"

"Yes."

"What do you do?"

"Nothing. How about you?"

"Same."

"Takes up all my time just doing nothing."

"I know."

"So is it a deal?"

"Yeah. Now buzz off."

***

I stay at home all week. I stare at the ceiling. I write out an entire 1,350-page novel in my head, scrawling letters onto the creeping blackness of the wall. I can see tiny mushrooms spread in a corner, and I have christened them all with individual names and likenesses and specific character traits. I have become intimate with my ceiling. One night I find my mind swaying to other walls and to the floor. Even in inanimation, I am unable to remain loyal, whatever that might mean. Fidelity is an insurance company, not a state of being. Still, it has been quiet upstairs for the entire week now and so I find myself drifting out cautiously towards the beach. Long Beach. A good hour's walk from where I am. I turn corners prying beforehand to avoid potential crossfire. I duck the some-times stray bullet in my mind, and walk down caressing the walls, all the way to Ocean Boulevard.

I can immediately feel the spray of surf and tiny dew drops of oil from the refinery off the shore. I step down onto the vast and deserted beach and stare at the chimneys bellowing packetfuls of cigarette smoke by the second. It is an artificial island, all lit up gaily and onerously, its mechanical monstrosities chugging up and down, thieving crude oil from fathomless seas. It is so close, this sci-fi horror, as to be able to touch it from a speckled shore. The water is thick black and lugubrious with salt and sunlessness. I walk the length of the beach, feeling the tiny particles ooze through the holes in my soles with much glee.

At the far end I can see the convention centre and the ship *Queen Mary* anchored for all posterity. I think of the futility of its efforts as it tries to break out of its chains and explore the seven seas. Instead, it is a museum piece, the darkly churning water a protective glass from curious onlookers with cameras and instant flashes.

I am thinking of Lawrence of Arabia on the *Queen Mary* on his passage to India in search of the jewel in the crown. I give old Morris the credit for much imagination, but this is a new low, even for one who has heard every sixty-second pitch in Hollywood. In every boardroom in Culver City and Burbank, in the back of mail rooms, over lunch at Spago, and at AA meetings across town. I try to laugh, but I have misplaced my sense of humour, lost at birth, discarded along with the umbilical, some tell me.

***

Even as I approach home, I can tell the fat man is at it again. I go straight up and thump loudly. He opens the door, looking a carbon copy of the other day.

"I'm home."

"Ok."

All is quiet now. I begin my second novel. I'm running out of space on the ceiling. I'm going to have to stay home I know.

***

In the morning, there is a timid knock on the door. It is the first time I know what a knock on this door sounds like. It is a strange sound. I open the door fully, expecting a welcome barrage of something to end the day. Instead I am presented with a small, petite woman in T-shirt and torn jeans, wrinkled face saddened beyond grief. She has a package in her hands. I can tell by the largeness of her purple eye, even through her sunglasses, and from the various bruises across her face, that it is her.

A small infinity passes between us before she proffers the package. I open it silently. A small slice of what looks like fresh apple-pie. She never once looks at me, hiding instead behind large sunglasses that veiled her eyes insufficiently. We stand there until I don't know how long, and then she turns around in silence and walks back up the stairs.

***

We are at the fifth hole, third stroke on a par five at the Rancho Park Golf Course in the Hillcrest Country Club, just south of Beverly Hills. Morris is setting up his swing and I am standing aloof, sweltering under the unrepentant sun.

"I'm afraid I can hardly help you if you don't want to help yourself. I got enough writers barking up my sleeve to have to worry about who's gonna leave a meeting halfway with a stolen apple."

"Plastic."

He misses the ball. Angry, he sets up again, flexing now somewhat arthritic muscles.

"What?"

"Plastic," I said."I should know. I tried to eat it."

"Do you want to get it made or not?"

"Not if you're gonna put Peter O'Toole in flowing robes and headdress on the *Queen Mary* on his way to India to find the jewel in the crown."

"Peter's too old. I'm thinking Bruce Willis."

I realise we are speaking different languages. I drop the subject.

"Is there a home or someplace like that for battered wives?"

"Why? You got one?"

Funny.

"No. But I know one."

"Where? In South Central or whichever other shooting range you live in?"

"Long Beach."

"Same difference."

"Yes or no?"

"No."

"So what am I supposed to do?"

"Stick out of other people's business."

He hits it hard. It swerves starboard and crash lands near a clump of trees. This is not the best of times to ask for some money, I know, but I do anyway.

"Why?"

This seems an ostensibly moronic question to me, but I answer it nevertheless.

"Because I don't have any obviously."

"So what am I supposed to do?"

"Advance me some."

"On what? For what?"

"On me. For me."

"On one condition."

"I'm listening."

"I'm representing a package deal for a new cable

company. Providing them 52 movies of the month. You know the stuff. *Deadly Poison*. The *So-and-So Story*. *Final Escape*. The *True Story of So-and-So*. That sort of thing, I need a fiction. Along the same lines. Erotic thriller, suspense drama. The nanny did it to save her unborn child from the clutches of a fictional foreign regime. With one soft nude scene, topless but hidden by well-placed curtains and sheets and bashful arms. One car chase down Topanga Canyon or Mulholland, it doesn't matter which, and a final resolution at Griffith Park, looking out across L.A. in the sunset genre. Everything and the kitchen sink and a twelve-inch knife thrown in for good measure. Think you can do it?"

"No. I don't like the kitchen sink genre."

"She'll probably die from his beatings if you don't do something soon."

"It's for me."

"Yeah, right. It always is. Yes or no?"

"No."

"Fine. I'll call Loquacious. He did a great job with *Whose Child Is It Anyway? The Sally Sperm Story.*"

He drives off into Pico Boulevard, swerving dangerously close to the Beverly Glen Hospital. I look at him and shrug.

"Loquacious is sick," I hasten to add to his misfortune.

"With what?"

"Verbal diarrhoea."

"He has been since birth."

"I know."

We head toward the hospital. In silence. There is something redeeming about intelligent men who fashion themselves after the lowest common denominator. It adds to my perception of Morris' vulnerability to know that his prostration for pelf was at least honest, and without the conceit of assumed art.

"By the way." I'm curious to know, "Did you think Baby X should have ended up with Sally Sperm?"

"How the hell should I know? I never read the damn thing."

***

I am flat out on my mind, spread across its empty spaces, lying on my back on a cold carpetless floor, concocting nothing. The secretary from Morris' office called earlier saying the story had to be set in Anytown, USA, that generic food stamp of the poor and the hungry. Anytown, USA meant that labour costs in Virginia or the Bayou or whatever could be tapped, instead of exorbitant city guild and union rates. Anytown, USA. What a great address this is. I repeat it to myself again and again. Anytown, USA. I think of the protagonist presenting his business card to the waitress in some anonymous Hicksville town. John Smith. No name street. Anytown, USA.

Suddenly, and without any warning; a crash. A loud thumping crash of body against furniture, rattling lamps and breaking vases. A loud, but brief and modest shriek in lieu of paper-thin walls. Then a nine-month pregnant pause, followed by the gasps and groans of a painfully induced labour. I stare at the empty page. There are only the words FADE IN written at the top corner. I try and shut out the image, but the slap is ferocious this time. Hard and ringing. I close my ears forcefully, palm flat against temple. I hear nothing momentarily, then screams and abuses and the crashing of fragile objects. I hear glass shatter even through my defenses, and with a great big thud and roll onto a weak floor, the concerto climaxes.

I can see its conductor now, towering over her like Golgotha. She will cook his eggs just right in the morning. Never again, she promises too, will she burn his toast.

This is Anytown, USA. I begin my prostitution.

***

Morris is clearly not pleased. Imaginary vapours emanate from his nostrils. He taps gingerly, yet impatiently on his mahogany table, vast as the Pacific. Ten weeks have passed since I started my rounds, and already the pimp was getting restless.

"Ten weeks. Ten weeks I tell you. I ain't seen nothing yet."

"I'm working on it."

"How far are you?"

"I've reached 'Fade In.'"

"Is this some kind of joke?"

"I'll get it done."

"It was due last week."

"I know."

"You're fired."

"You can't fire somebody who has no job."

"You're right."

"Tomorrow. I'll have it for you tomorrow."

"You're gonna write a 100-page screenplay overnight?"

"110."

"How do you know?"

"Give 10 pages for the kitchen sink."

"And the whammos?"

"Every ten pages as promised."

"No intellectual stuff."

"God forbid."

"No inner thoughts, no introverted bullshit, and no

ten page descriptions of moods, feelings and sunsets."

"I don't write about sunsets."

"There has to be one."

"Page 54."

"How do you know?"

"I don't."

"The car chase?"

"A Chevy '79 runs down a BMW on Coldwater Canyon."

"I prefer Mulholland."

"Too bad."

"What's it called?"

"Anytown, USA."

***

The Chevy '79 pulls itself north on Highway 1. It is still early in the day and the traffic is somewhat calm. I do not know where I am headed, I know only that I want to hug the coastline as I get to it. Pacific skies, blue as the water isn't, greet open arms in topless cars. I think of my conversation with Morris. I am amazed at my own ability to create nonsense. Los Angeles was about as much Anytown, USA as Xanadu or Atlantis for that matter. Yet somehow, it seemed apt, as if all the Anytowns, USA gathered here for a large convention long ago and forgot to go back home, or got stuck eastbound on the 10.

Just outside of Santa Barbara and I turn back. The entire story is in my head. I have only to write it. On paper.

***

I stare at the two opening words. A long period has since passed and metal has not as yet struck paper. Then, as if on cue, the show begins. I have become desensitized to it — to all the noises, slaps and cries. I keep typing. More and more forceful with each blow. Sometimes in sync to it, sometimes not. I hear entire orchestrations and capture them. Briefly it stops, then starts again. And again and again. I allow myself a temporary respite, flex the fingers shortly and await the music one more time. It never fails to disappoint. On and on and again still more. I can see her eyes swell before me. I can see a tiny slip of blood ooze its vengeance out of the corner of a lash. I can see the scratchings and maulings of belt on skin, bottle on skin, flesh on skin. I am the hidden microphone, the fly-on-the-wallpaper. I can record her cries for help and mercy and forgiveness. I can imprint footsteps, choreograph movements, justify my silence and that of neighbours. I record everything impassionately, calculatedly, a court stenographer in a soporific case with little or no excitement value. I am equipped with radar and transmitters and all manner of technology that allows me to type as fast as the blows and often more furious and painful. I am the documentarian of her fate as I pry into her journals with subjective ink; black and indelible.

In the morning I drop off the screenplay with the secretary.

***

I swing towards a diner off Sunset Boulevard. I watch the twenty-foot murals of "Hollywood Legends" pass me by, complete with Humphrey Bogart in grey Fedora. A young boy is pissing at his feet. I watch the tourists outside Mann's Chinese theatre, cameras flashing as they find favourite stars on sidewalks. I watch the billboards and larger-than-life signs as they look down on me; stuck as

I am in traffic. I am numbed by car horns and ambulance sirens. The smog is so thick and heavy today it sits like icing on a cake. I can carve out my own piece and make neat little blocks for ten million others and still have room to spare. Everything around me is ugly. Flat and ugly and characterless. I suddenly realize as I read an out-of-state license plate that I have to get out. My lungs are choking for air, for cigarette smoke not polluted by exhausts, for an eclectic denominator and not the lowest common one. I realise at last that Anytown, USA is the giant cookie-cutter mentality of the chips on a conveyor belt that is chewing me up. Each cookie had to have exactly the same amount of chips, the same weight, the same size, and even the same palatable taste. And hence the formula. It was this anonymous Everyman's shoes that I was being slipped into, unconsciously seduced by numbers, not words.

Meanwhile, two abortions and forty years later, Patsy Pringle serves me piping hot generic coffee at the generic diner. She has been working the day shift since I got here which seems far longer than it really is. She swills her diet Coke and nervously draws on her low-tar cigarette waiting patiently for her big break. She passes out her portfolio, five years antiquated, to anyone who might happen to mention the movies. The years have taken their toll and the grey has already come to her very bleached blonde hair, but she refuses to do "elderly" roles for fear of being typecast. She tells me her recent woes. A casting agent who tried to rape her. The same one she went to last month. A producer she slept with but still didn't get the walk-on-job. Three months ago she sent off $100 to a post box number. The advertisement in a trade paper said it was only for Screen Actors Guild fees, and that a role was "guaranteed". A security guard at a major studio she had to go down on to join the phalanx of Groupies that waited six hours to meet a big star on location. She points to her almost wrinkle-free face, and the tiny dots from her collagen injections and fat suction. The silicon in her breasts is leaking she tells me, but as long as it happens very slowly, at least they'll remain firm for a while yet. Her nose has been done three times as she was able to con the insurance into thinking the surgery wasn't elective, but induced due to whiplash from a near fatal car accident. She shows me "before" and "after" shots and explains how tubes removed fat from her thighs and how her sagging bottom no longer sags and why. She retells with immense pride the fact that she has lost three more pounds in the last six weeks, and I look at her and mentally calculate at what rate her 80 pound frame will disappear entirely. She has less time than me.

I pay her the check, leave a hefty tip and exit. I know I will not see her again, unless of course she made it big.

***

The call came sharply in the morning, as I expected. Three hours later I sat across his mahogany.

"I'd like to say that I'm angry, but I'm not. In fact, I'm pissed. Not at you, but at me, for allowing you to waste my time with all your intellectual pretentious bullshit. The public doesn't want to see other peoples' problems on the screen dammit! They have enough problems of their own. Take your shit from the secretary and get the hell outta here before I blow your head off."

I am not exactly presented with choices here, so I do as I'm told.

***

I watch the fat man leave on his Harley Davidson and slip the screenplay under her door, knocking loudly. I leave before she appears.

I pack what little I have. Two pairs of everything, like Noah unto his ark. A typewriter, some loose sheafs of paper. A small hard bag. Everything I own is in that one bag. I am ready for travel again, minus compass, map, guide book and direction.

I sit against the wall and stare at the ceiling with shut eyes. Hours pass into the night. I hear the roar of the motor bike as it pulls into the sidewalk. I begin counting a fast one hundred. At sixty-eight, it starts again. A bit slow today.

I shut my eyes tightly. The shouts and groans and cries ring through my self and up my feet and the pain is no longer just on paper. My eyes shut tighter and tighter in the vain hope of closing it out. I do not ever remember it continuing this long. I realize it stops tonight because it is *he* that is tired. I can almost hear her breathing heavily. Gasping for thin air, rarefied with much abuse.

***

The knock comes as expected in the early dawn of late night. I pick up my belongings and open the door wide. Outside, she is standing, bag in hand. We look at each other only momentarily before we head for my car.

*****

Searching For Gauquin

I am asleep on my back, flat out on the azure blue crystalline waters of the South Pacific. The French South Pacific, to be more precise. I am here today on Pt. Despecheurs (Point of Fishing) because I want to be away from the rest. It is not the best of beaches as beaches go. The black sand is a novelty, a legacy of the once actively volcanic Tahitian islands. But it is rocky and unkempt and scrags of rebel grass protrude from adamant weather and wave-beaten stone. The entire width is barely a human's length long, but it stretches a few miles into oblivion.

I am on my back because I cannot think with my face submerged, crying out for air. I am thinking because it is the one thing I know how to do. I think all the time, overtime. It is my main vice. I am thinking of corners of this planet as yet unexplored, of cities unworn and untread, of people unfamiliar to unfamiliar faces. I am thinking as always of home; a home, whatever that might mean and wherever that might be.

***

The current is fierce. For a vast body of water supposedly as still as the Pacific today's ebb and flow is rather strong. It drags me away even as I allow it to. I can feel it pull my body in directions new. The sun is straight above my eyes and even though they're shut with a vengeance, I squint narrowly. It is a powerful undercurrent and every so many feet I can feel my body touch something — coral or sand or rockbottom perhaps. The current has dragged me far away today. I feel the shore caress my back with its warm wet sand urging me to awake.

Tenuously, I do so. Propping myself up on my elbows, I am blinded by the ferocity of the light for the first few moments but when I finally get to see, I see why the current was so adamant.

It is a living, breathing cliché. A small, black sand promontory juts out into the coral. A mango tree of ample proportions anchored on its soil, tilts its branches deceptively out towards the water. In the shade underneath it, is a small rickety wooden bench. She is sitting upon it.

Her bikini is immodest even for a French Polynesian. Her skin is two shades lighter than the sand, tanned permanently since birth. She is reading a rather large book that sits precariously on her knees. In front of her is a pile of some green fruit which I can't identify. She sees me, squatting barely a few feet from her, staring point-blank, dilated pupils and all.

She plucks a small green round fruit from off the bunch and brings it to her lips. They are thick and full. She puts the fruit to her mouth. Watching her eat, I'm suddenly taken hungry. I walk up and sit on the bench beside her. She offers me the fruit.

"What is it?" I need to know.

"Quenette," she replies demonstrating with a casual grace how it is eaten. I attempt to pluck away at the fruit much as she did. Quenette after quenette passes between our lips. The sun comes low, eye-level, then sinks without a trace, leaving a purple haze over the horizon.

"What are you reading?" I ask.

"Gauguin's diary," she offers.

"What does he say?"

"That Bora-Bora, where he lived and worked was his second chance, his second redemption, his new life."

"What's the book called?"

"Noa Noa."

"Do you like his work?"

"Only what he painted in Tahiti. His French art was not so good."

She giggles. I haven't taken my eyes off her.

"Why are you here?" she asks.

"I'm searching for Gauguin myself," I reply.

"Why?"

"I don't know."

"How did you get here?"

"The current brought me."

"From where?"

"From over there," I point to where I started out today. I can barely make out my things in the distance.

"So you live there?" she giggles, pointing to my stuff.

"For today, yes."

"And yesterday?"

"Wherever the current took me."

"You're from very far away."

"Yes."

"How far?"

"From over there," again I point to my stuff.

"Where were you from before you were from there?"

"From somewhere else."

"What have you been doing?"

"Searching."

"For what?"

"I don't know."

"You a painter?"

"No."

"Then what?"

"Dreamer."

She stares at me, not quite sure whether to laugh or to be serious. She is ravishingly beautiful. No wonder the old world was in so much of hurry to find the new one. Her straight long black hair hangs open to her waist, her large and inquisitive black eyes are full of questions. Her name is Francesca Saminadme, half French, half Tahitian, all sin.

***

We are at the Taina Bar, moving to some heady Tahitian music. She swerves like a cat on a bend at a hundred miles an hour, hips swivelling unforgivingly. She knows everyone here. The dolt who smiles all the time and scratches the dried skin on his forehead. The buck-toothed DJ and the five guitar-playing Sumo-wrestling musicians, all grinning wider than anatomically possible. Her boyfriends and girlfriends all pay their respects, even grinding a hip or two in unison. Everyone rolls their own cigarettes and ash covers the make-shift dance floor. Drunk tourists, red-faced and stripped of all cash, glue their eyes onto gyrating bodies. The barman calls himself Jean-Melville and whips up cocktails faster than he fled Toulouse. Francesca is rapidly kissed full-flushed by men and women alike, and everything in between as well.

More drinks are ordered. We sit at a cramped table and sniff Drum tobacco from pipes. I am drifting. I am thinking again of why I am here and what I hope to find. Every which way I look at it, I come up with scratch. I am attempting to get lost but keep finding myself again.

A tap on the shoulder. A tall, hirsutely hare-lipped muscular man in a helmet, upturned collars and enormous breasts. He had been eyeing me all evening, mad as a hatter for stealing Francesca for a few dances. There had been rumblings earlier, but nothing had come of it. A push and a shove on the floor I let pass as being the fault of the crowd. He's a she all right, auditioning for Orlando in Virginia Woolfe's novel, only not as pretty. He wants to have it out. A duel unto death for the fair hand of the indomitable, the incomparable Francesca.

We step outside into the humid night. A crowd follows. Jean-Melville is quick to assume desertion and is upon me with a fat check. I point to Orlando, she points to me. He refuses to let us pass through the gate without it being cleared first. Orlando shoves Jean-Melville. His Toulouse accent gets the better of him and he mutters incomprehensibly. No one argues with Orlando. Francesca has already fled to another pair of arms, man or woman I do not know. I watch her swivel in the commotion. I am hypnotized by the sway. To and fro, to and fro, it is mesmerizing. The chaos peaks and before I know it, I am on the floor.

I see stars. Kaleidoscope ones. Merging and meshing together, dissolving neatly and reappearing. I hear foreign tongues and more strokes and slaps. Suitably loud whistles and catcalls and the best of French colloquialism is on display. Gradually, I see galaxies and shooting stars and black holes and entire milky ways. All subtitled in French.

***

The gendarmes at the corner of Avenue Bruat and Rue des Poilus Tahitians are not pleased. The police station is abuzz with inactivity, a myriad mirages shimmering off the glaze from hot tarmac roads. Their blue shorts dangle loosely about their knees, their tobacco is rolled into a sloppy pouch from which it is lit, their eyes are droll and droopy and the afternoon sun is unrepentant. I am not exactly about to allow them their siesta.

They listen to my story with due pomp and ceremony. Orlando attempts to interject every few words and flails her arms about passionately, countering every point I make. I insist we stick to English and the gendarmes agree for the sake of brevity. I plead my poverty and ignorance of the ways of the South Pacific and state firmly that I should be set free with enough to buy *le baguette* and fare on *le truck* to Faa'a Aeroport or else they will be hearing from my Consul General in the nearest township, which incidentally, is not near at all. Orlando then begins her version and naturally it is quite different from mine. She protests at having had to pay the entire tab implying that my passing-out was too conveniently timed, and demands that I should repay her full cost. She is not in a good mood, I can tell. The muscles are rippling under her checked shirt, and the moustache is not pleased either.

An hour or so of banter and much negotiation and translation later, the gendarme with a bristling moustache to match Orlando's, comes up with an ingenious plan.

Why don't we all simply pay our respective shares, split it one-third and go our separate ways, in the interest of international amity? I pounce upon the idea and dig up the few thousand francs I have, displaying the notes on the counter. A calculator, that irredeemable tool that crosses every national boundary of miscommunication, is brought out, the numbers are added up and I am short by a few francs so miserable as to sneeze at. Unfortunately, they are not the humouring kind. I must pay the full third.

We settle on making amends by doing some typing. Orlando is paid off by the bristling moustache and I am marched off to an old Olivetti typewriter that wouldn't attract a flea in a flea market. The letters are all in French of course, but I swear I know how it works. I am given a few pages of gibberish in long hand that I am to type into the official police report. In the interest of inter-national amity, I begin to do so without complaint and without pulling off Consul General strings and the like. I busy myself scrutinizing accents on passive and posses-sive verbs and type out the report of some poor dolt's lost scooter and misplaced helmet. In the next room I can hear snoring already. An almost lazy, deeply sonorous kind of snoring, prostrate, soporific, dormant like volca-noes too tired to erupt. I await my chance, and slip out the door, running all the way down Avenue Bruat until I reach the Boulevard Pomare.

I go to the Vaima Perles supermarket, find the Cambio, and exchange the traveller's cheques that were tucked inside my socks. I make my way to the *le truck* stop and await the first transport to nowhere. I sit at the back and watch as Tahiti unfolds itself to me. We drive past Venus Point with its immaculately crowded black sand dunes, we go through the Blow Hole Arahono, waiting full five

minutes for it to erupt. We trek to the Vaiharuru waterfall
and watch as well-dressed tourists plan their group
photographs with a bilingual guide who sneers behind
their back. We laugh as a group of German tourists break
out in a loud argument about the cost of the local beer.
We work our way past Taravao and Papeari until the bus
stops at the Gauguin Museum. I get off for no apparent
reason.

Nubile women sucking the pulp of mango. Deer
poised for flight. Little brown boys staring wide-eyed and
vacant. Women plaiting each other's hair. Each canvas an
interplay of colours more warm and luscious than I could
ever imagine. A loving brushstroke, tenderly rapt into the
local haute cuisine, the indigenousness of it all. A thirteen-
year-old Tahitian girl. His wife or mistress or saviour or
some such thing. I stare at the image, a nascent moustache
worn with much pride of place. A tilt of the neck
heavenward, the long black hair adorned with flowers. A
lazy cloth swung around the curves of her torso. I think
of him here a hundred or so years ago and imagine this
misplaced, mixed breed accountant who left his family
and children and the cold anonymity of France to come
here to paint his life away. I imagine his reception; warm
and welcome, with a fare paid for by the good taxpayers
of his adopted country in the pursuit of a much nobler
aspiration of Art with a capital A. I imagine him if he
were to make the journey today. Certain anonymity.
Besides the colours are white, not brown, the blue only
reflected off skies, not sea beds, the coral all trodden upon
by feet asunder, and the costs all blown out of proportion.
How would he have survived?

****

That night I stroll down his street. Not even the respectability of an Avenue, but merely a rue Gauguin. It is
littered by men in drag. There is the Lido, Le Club 5, the
Piano Bar. There is even a Moulin Rouge. Every few feet
is a stiletto, high and unbalanced by broad shoulders and
much lipstick.

Her name is Alessandra, long for Alex. Her wig is
immaculately blonde as it falls about her airplane-wing
shoulders. The stilettos are worn by too much tarmac and
unforgiving potholes. Her purse is small and functional,
her lips anything but. She is hungry. We make our way
to the waterfront for a shared crēpe or two by the
Roulettes. She does not want to be seen here, it will lower
her image to be spotted with a foreigner sharing a crēpe
at an outdoor food stall as cheap as this is. But hunger
prevails over modesty.

He was raised in the island of Huahine by parents who
treated him as a girl as is much the custom here. He came
here to Papeete as an eighteen-year-old, seeking fame and
fortune, but found only foreigners.

"What do you think of Gauguin?" I inquire, with a
mouthful of crēpe still undone.

"What is there to think? The man is a genius. I love
him."

"Why do you think that?"

"Have you seen his work?"

"Yes. Only his Tahiti stuff though."

"The rest is no good, no good at all."

"Why did he come here?"

"Is that not obvious?"

"Today, I don't know anymore."

"Aaah, but monsieur, you have a point. Today. Maybe
not. But even when he came 100 years ago, he did not

like Tahiti, he went to Bora Bora."

"I know."

"Have you been to Bora Bora?"

"No. Will you take me?"

"It will cost you."

"I know."

We are on the catamaran speeding through to emerald islands. I am reminded of every Tahiti brochure I had ever seen and discarded. On Bora Bora, Alessandra takes me by hand to his hut. It is still there, quite intact as it was a century earlier. I enter it with some reverence and awe, not quite knowing the correct protocol for such situations. I look out from his little window onto the gentle lapping of the sea on the shore. Suddenly there is a light rain. A squall of which Tahiti seems to have aplenty each day. I am immensely driven by the music of the sounds as they rise and fall and rise again, coming and going and coming again as though orchestrated by some invisible conductor. Here, in Gauguin's house, at last I feel free.

I remove my journal from my bag, wet the nib of the fountain pen on the tip of my tongue and begin writing. I lean the book against the sill, prop it up with one hand and scribble furiously with the other. It has been months since parched hands found strength to write again. The block is broken, much drivel and nonsense now flows like larva let loose after eons spent lying low. I am making love now, in some primal scream of my own pent-up angst, and ink flows brutal against the virgin whiteness of paper, as it succumbs, pleads, but allows the seduction. I spore forth with vengeance, wreaking havoc, flipping pages, numbing sensation, understanding the search.

Alessandra leaves me to my own.

***

Hours to go until flight. I am sitting at the Cafe Le Retro on the Boulevard Pomare, across the wharf in the middle of Papeete, smoking Gauloises, drinking Hinano *biere*. An old man with a week-long stubble, unruly hair, a shaky gait and foul breath clumps himself before me. We stare at each other a few moments. He looks vaguely familiar.

"I hear you're searching for me?"

"Who are you?"

"Paul Gauguin."

"But you're dead."

"No. I'm on sabbatical."

"I see. Who told you I'm looking for you?"

"Word gets around. What do you want?"

"I want to know what you were searching for all those years and whether you ever found it?"

"No. I'm still searching. Why else do you think I'm still alive?"

"But what are you searching for?"

"I don't know."

"Me neither."

"We're doomed then, you and I. We're doomed to spend the rest of our lives searching for something we don't know."

"But we'll know when we find it."

"So the theory goes anyway."

"Want a beer?"

"A Carlsberg please. I don't drink the local rubbish. Do you know Prince Hinoi has his own Avenue. So does that idiot de Gaulle. But what do I get? A rue! A bloody rue! The swine! I put Tahiti on the map once and for all and I don't even get an avenue named after me."

"Is that what you want then? An avenue named after you?"

"Why do you think they mutinied on the bounty? Who do you think brought Stevenson and Melville and all the other guys here? Who introduced these artists to this paradise? Without me there would be no Treasure Island."

"Or Moby Dick," I venture.

"Exactly! Do you know Destremeau?"

"No."

"No one else knows him either. A bloody insignificant commandant or something. He has his own avenue. A big one all the way to the airport. What do I get?"

"You do have a museum," I point out, making a brave attempt at detente.

"How can you make a museum of words or of politicians or of commandants? Of course I have a museum. Can you hang Treasure Island from a wall?"

"You do have a point." The detente is not working.

"It's the least they can do. Where are you staying?"

"The Teamo Hostel."

"Expensive?"

"All Tahiti is expensive. This place is a dive."

"Inspiring?"

"No. But your house on Bora-Bora was to me."

"Why?"

"I don't know."

"I'll tell you. You were in trouble. Heap loads of trouble. Not a word written in months. Not a bad line of poetry. Not even a Dear John or Jill letter inscribed in maudlin verse. You were all washed up and dried out and run out of words. Sometimes it doesn't take anything out of the ordinary. It wasn't the sea or the trees or Alessandra or anything like that."

"What was it then?"

"The same thing you're searching for."

"And that is...?"

"The search itself."

He sculls his Carlsberg in a hurry, throws a few francs onto the table and flees as quickly as he came. I watch him disappear down his own rue, lamenting the avenues given to others, swearing under his breath.

Francesca sits where he once warmed the chair. She is dressed up for a night out on the town.

"Who were you talking to?"

"No-one."

"Do you always talk to no-one?"

"Always."

"I came to return you your share of the dinner. Maybe one day when I come to wherever it is you live you can take me out. Where do you live?"

"I don't know as yet."

"Do you have an address?"

"No."

She tenderly places the notes next to his and rises to kiss me on the cheek. She treats it like a quenette and sucks its life-bloody dry. She is a walking painting, hung by her own thread on a mobile wall. She turns to leave.

"By the way, did you find him?"

"Who?"

"Gauguin."

I am silent for a moment. As a child I always believed we had a certain number of words granted us upon birth. A quota system if you wish. I was always afraid of talking too much, for fear of using up my quota too soon and then having to spend the rest of my life in grim silence.

"No," I mutter finally, "He found me."

***

When the Demon Ate the
Moon

*W*ayan Surma leaned conspiratorially towards me. His thin eyebrows plucked away at his receding hairline and arched themselves like a taut bow. He looked around him furtively, the white of his security guard uniform only adding to the aura. His breath wafted its Bali Hai Pilsener Beer freshness across my face like the surf at Kuta beach.

"Do you know the story about the night the moon was eaten by a demon?"

Without waiting for a reply, he began. "A long time ago you see, legend has its story that the beautiful and abundant gods of Bali possessed the Tirta Amerta, or the water of eternity. Obviously as you can imagine now the demons who lurked badly away on earth also wanted to be possessing the sacred water that insured they too would never die. This water was paradise. Like Bali is, or rather, was."

A faraway look came into his eyes. He stared out across Kuta Bay at the rapidly and ominously rising swell of the surf. His short stockiness and well-built torso belied his age and lent much credence to his nostalgia. Heaving a sigh, he continued.

"Now this water as you can only imagine was kept away in a very secret place. But somehow it came to pass that Kala Rau, one of the demons lurking on earth found out about his paradise and went out in search of it. He was not of this place. He was foreign. He was evil and he possessed many magics that we did not know, and he was to bring dread and downfall on all the Balinese peoples lives forever and eternity. Somehow travelling the seas and skies with his tall ships and wings, he found this paradise, snatched it away, but very gradually and slowly only you see, bit by bit, very very slowly, he had it and took it away with him to his palace."

"Excuse me saar, buy sarong?" we are interrupted by the sarong seller. I wave her away. "Buy sarong saar, cheap sarong, looking nice on you." I wave her away again. "Maybe short pants, or something? Very cheap, only twenty thousand rupiah." I ignore her upon Wayan's request. She moves on to other less irritable tourists not halfway through listening to a Balinese myth. I swill the Bintang beer and wait until the faraway look in his eyes returns to the present.

"But Dewi Ratih, the goddess of the moon, you see, she was very very alert and saw what happened because obviously only she was in the sky and could see everything. She told Dewa Ciwa about what had happened and he in turn sent the fiery war god Indra to sort out the matter. Now Indra, as I said was very very fiery and he went about searching for this lost paradise and searched long and hard but could not find it. In its place you see very many demons had taken over. Too many to even count. They began to outnumber the gods themselves."

I look out this time at the beach. Topless women, white as alabaster, soaking up the sun. Men with matted blond locks making their way towards the water, surfboard in tow. Germans, Australians, British, Dutch and the occasional American. White bodies on white beaches, occupying much sand and space, interspersed only barely by the stocky brown of peddlers of all wares.

"Hey Rastaman, want wood carving?" I turn this time and say no.

"How about very very nice bong? Cheap. Very cheap. Ok for you take only forty thousand Rupiah."

"I don't want, thank you," I reply.

Big mistake. My first week here and the novice blues are showing. We are suddenly surrounded by more bong sellers than I had seen bongs before in my life. All types of bongs. A man fishing, wearing a typical conical Vietnamese hat, and suddenly the hat opens and the fish pole sticks into his head, transforming it into a bong. Mothers carrying replaceable children that are removed and stuck into their stomachs for the tourist to smoke his stuff from off the mouths of babies and into mothers' wombs. I am not impressed. Wayan has been calm until now. He cannot wave his countrymen away yet he shows his stripes and anger loudly in hidden nuances, decibels only the locals can hear. Gradually, after much growling in Balinese, not Indonesian as he repeatedly informs me, they disperse.

"But Dewa Indra finally found Kala Rau the demon. He was on the beach, about to swallow the immortal water. Without any second thought only Indra fired away his arrow which went straight into Kala Rau's neck completely separating his body from his head. The body then fell to this mortal and polluted earth and was immediately transformed into a wooden bell, what we call Kulkul. However, very very interesting thing happened. His head, you see was still intact, because legend has it that a tiny drop of the Tirta Amerta had already touched his throat. Hence his head alone became immortal."

Wayan pauses. Not for breath, but for effect, I realize. He summons the bartender and we get refills. We are on the beach itself, sitting on small wooden chairs at a cane bar, surrounded by a few lazy foreigners and tourists too tired or bothered to get wet or tanned. A maze of bodies are sprawled out around me, all blubbery fat, white as rancid milk, getting massaged from old and speculatively tiny brown hands. The masseurs, mostly old, toothless women, all wear the pyramid hat of the rice-farmer of a distant generation. Their dexterous fingers weave and transform rolling flesh into something a little more re-laxed, and consequently, more rolling.

"Now Kala Rau as you can imagine was very very angry. He swore to chase Dewi Ratih wherever she went. So more and more ships and sails and wings and fiery breaths and rolling flesh arrived to devour the beauty of this paradise, only irony is, they did not come seeking revenge, only came seeking immortality and a good time. Urged on by his fellow foreigners, Kala Rau found Dewi Ratih one day, and in his immense lust and greed he swallowed her wholly only. But what he forgot was that he did not have body any more — no way in which to digest the new culture in his system. He was all head, no heart, nothing. So after many many struggle, Dewi

Ratih was manage to slip out of Kala Rau's head and become herself again."

Two Australian women are bargaining fiercely with a ring merchant. A few more show up and display their wooden boxes full of shiny wares. One of them holds up a ring with "Bali" emblazoned across it.

"Look, look. A Bali ring. How appropriate. Something to show back home where we've been."

"No, no, the yin and yang is more appropriate. Its their religious thing. How cute."

"Twenty thousand Rupiah."

"We will give you ten for the Bali ring and the yinyang thing."

"Oh no, no, no, very very cheap madam. No can."

"Sorry then."

"OK. But you get very very cheap."

"How did Dewi Ratih manage such a feat?" I offer, hoping it didn't end there. "Well, like I say only, a man, however much a demon, with no heart and no body all head with no understanding of the local mythology cannot devour our gods. Dewi Ratih knew she would escape someday and she did. But to this day, the evil Kala Rau chases her everyday — unforgiving, unrepentant. You see tonight. After many years again, he will attempt to devour her."

"How?" I want to know.

"You will see. I have to go now, patrol the other five bars on the beach. Is my job you see. Too very very many foreigners getting drunk all day and getting sunstroke and all that. Meet me tonight at 2 a.m. at the Hard Rock Cafe on Raya Legian."

"The Hard Rock Cafe? Here in Bali?"

"Yes. It is just before McDonalds, almost opposite KFC.

2 a.m. If you cannot be making it, make sure you page me and tell me so OK?"

Wayan saunters off towards the next bar, taking in the beach scene in one sweeping glance just as he leaves. I am sinking into my Bintang. Even the local brew does not raise my spirits. Someone presses my arm.

"Massage saar. Good massage. Like this."

Before I know it, my sore arms and legs are being pressed into all oblivion.

"No. No. Thank you. I don't have any money."

"No problem. You give what you want. For good luck only."

I look at her. The age and worry and the toll of a tiny shack in a crowded Denpasar street are etched into her forehead. Her pinnacle hat casts long shadows onto her face, wrinkled by much unrepentant sun and neglect. Her eyes are small and ten thousand crows feet spread themselves at the corner in a perpetual glinting. Her fingers are tiny and nimble. They traipse up and across my arms, unhindered by my protest. She smiles. A many-toothless smile, burdened under too much flesh that needs kneading like dough.

"Tell me a story instead," I say. "I pay you for that."

"What type story you want to hear?"

"Your story. Your gods. Your land."

"Mister saar, is no longer our land. Look."

And with that she waves her tiny hands across the landscape. Camouflaged bodies dot every particle of sand and every crest of every surf. I see the signs. Speedo and Rip Curl and Coca Cola. We are in an Australian commercial for suntan lotion or Qantas Jetabout Tours.

"Ten thousand Rupiah."

"Sorry?" I am confused or sunstroked, I don't know

which.

"Ten thousand Rupiah and I tell you the story of Tektekan."

I think aloud. I convert quickly. That's just under $5 US, about 3 pounds, 125 baht, 40 Hong Kong dollars, 175 Indian rupees, 375 French Pacific francs and about 5 Australian dollars. I whip out crumpled notes from my pocket. Three Bintangs already down and that's six thousand Rupiah, which leaves me with exactly four more thousand to listen to the story of Tektekan. I offer them humbly, unable to bargain like most. She looks at them with scorn, but readily pockets the notes. She sits on a vacant stool beside me and orders a glass of water with much pomp and ceremony. It is placed before her with some contempt. She drinks quickly and heartily, and wipes away the residue with the end of her sarong that has seen better days.

"You sure you no want massage? For you only ten thousand."

"Tektekan," I remind her.

She shuts her eyes tightly and thinks momentarily. She begins the story, eyes still closed, as though in a trance of her own doing.

"Bali is Hindu place. Many many Hindu like India, where it all come from. Tektekan is only one of many dance we use to celebrate or work off plague or tell stories. Balinese people like telling story, especially with dance. It is our custom. This dance is no different, even though today Tektekan is mainly perform to show off to foreign tourists like you. Is no much more our dance than tourist dance. Still I tell you."

"I come from village of Kerambitan, where this dance is perform for people. It is main dance that has ritualistic, art and magic also as end of story will tell you. Word Tektekan not mean anything really. Just sound made when hitting Kentongan, which is like bamboo stick. Sound made is like "Tek" and so dance name. But story of dance more interesting."

She asks for more water. Obviously, she relishes her role of storyteller, as the amount is already paid, and she could just as well give me the censored, abridged version, or a recent pamphlet of the Bali Tourist Guide and leave. But instead, she faces the task as cultural ambassador of her tiny island and even tinier village of Kerambitan.

"You see saar, my village Kerambitan, long ago, had very bad bad big plague. This badness was always running away with our people and they falling sick right left and centre and dying just like that. Most of Kerambitan was wiping out due to plague. This plague not local plague like we see before. Some mystery illnessess like come from distant place to haunt good and poor people of Kerambitan. We never see this kind of badness and even local chief and local doctor not know what to do because it so foreign to us. Slowly and slowly it come and wiping away entire village and then moving onto new villages next door like Kukuh, Baturiti, Penarukan. In fact only most of Tabanan district was being wiping away. Very bad this plague."

"What did they do then?" I volunteered.

"Chief and people went to temple of Puseh where Dewa Wisnu stay. Wisnu is protector. So with high priest who we call Pemangku, the people all hold ceremony to ask for help. Then after many day, Wisnu come to earth and through Pemangku tell people of all village to perform ceremony with all religious use like instrument and everything, like Barong, Rangda, spear, umbrella, flag and like this only. After many like this performance of dance, tradition of Nektek born into our civilization and history. Slowly, this plague from far away was wiping out instead of it wiping us out."

"But, I don't ... uhm ... how did, what happens in the dance that it is so magical, so powerful? How did it chase away the plague?"

"Sacrifice."

"What do you mean?"

"Look see around you. There is imaginary line on beach which we local cannot cross. Our own people have drawn the line so we not come out on our own beach. This line keep them there and us here. If we want to give massage or sell sarong we have to shout to them from here. Listen."

I listen. The waves and shouts of "Excuse me" ring true her words. Repeatedly and again, the natives stand behind their line and shout to sunbathers to cross it to see their wares. Most never do. They lie still and inert, giving themselves up to gravity, as motionless as the sea is turbulent.

"You no can see but it sort of plague only. Slowly and one by one they come. When I was girl long long ago, this beach still mainly us. Now no longer. Like that plague in my village, we no see when or how it happens, but now we depend on plague to feed baby. No good. No good."

"What happened in Kerambitan?"

"The dance is very powerful. We use Calong Arang in version where the demon Ratna Mengali is wiping away by us. We use drums for music, also cenceng, flute, gong, and many many bamboo tube which become instrument to beat on like drum. Main reason for dance is Wali

— like in ceremony for gods and nature and people. Finally, with much sacrifice, we wiping out plague. But now, look, maybe it too late already."

I do not have the heart to look again. Instead, I escort myself away. My head is spinning with too much mythology and doom to cope with on a single day. I hear shouts of "Massage Saar" behind me, but I ignore it. "You want tell another story? Only three thousand this time. Fast-fast I tell."

I ponder my way towards the Raya Legian. A sort of Pigalle meets Montmartre in the bylanes of Chor Bazaar in Greenwich village. Everything you don't want and will never need you can buy here, with more hawkers per block than pedestrians. I am fed up of the insolence and persistence of these sellers of trinkets. I seek refuge from humanity and hop onto the next shared ride to the airport for a flight to West Sumbawa, in the province of East Nusa Tenggara.

I am to meet Indra Winasa, a long-time drunk and favourite son of the soil of these parts. A local raconteur with more yarns (all true, he always adds at each sentence) up his much inebriated memory than there are Nyales in Wanokaka.

He explains.

The most revered of all the myths (in these parts at least) is that of Pasola, the War Game. Just once a year, usually the seventh day or night after the full moon, in February or March, hundreds of thousands of Nyale, which is a kind of sea worm, appear mysteriously on the shore. The Rato, or head priest of the village, usually predicts the arrival of the Nyale with the keen sort of accuracy of anyone who owns a Gregorian calendar. Various festivities take place. Pajma — wherein two men box the daylights out of each other, Sumbanese style, and wild mass social dancing and folk singing, which is akin to all the sore-throated women of the province screaming together at their decibel-shattering off key best.

The next day is Pasola — a sort of wild man's polo, except there's no ball to hit, just each other. With the screaming women (from yesterday) at the fringes, hundreds of men on bare horseback carrying blunt wooden spears, attack in mock fury, throwing the "Pasolas" at each other.

The object of this game (ultimately) is to collect as many Nyale, intact, as they wash up on the shore. The Nyale, to the people of Kodi, Lamboya and Wanokaka are symbols of prosperity. The more that are caught intact, the greater the prosperity of the region. The more that are ruined or spoilt, the greater the risk of a failed harvest.

Indra Winasa takes two hours, twenty minutes and nine Bintangs to tell me so in as many inaudible words. I look around the makeshift tavern. All brown-skinned muscular squat men in sarongs. Not a foreigner washed up on this remote shore. The peace is unimaginable — I have not been here before.

Indra stares at an empty glass and summons a refill.

"Yes, and you can believe it, our prosperity depends on how many Nyale we capture without losing or hurting them."

"No," I offer "Your prosperity really relies on how many Nyale you can send back to wherever it is they came from."

Indra Winasa is too undone to comprehend.

****

That night, at the appointed hour, I met Wayan Surma

at the Hard Rock Cafe, and together we howled long and mercilessly at the moon, in an attempt to warn Dewi Ratih that the terrible Kala Rau was lurking in the shadows, ready to devour her. But no matter how hard we howled and how many fiercely patriotic drums were beaten, the greedy Kala Rau managed to slowly swallow Dewi Ratih wholly, until only a tiny sliver of a gold edge was visible. Wayan turned to me. His pain was almost palpable. His screams increased in tempo and frequency. I could only watch him. Darkness descended momentarily as the moon was obliterated. More drums were beaten than I had ever heard in my life. And surely enough, within moments, the good goddess, Dewi Ratih managed to slip out of Kala Rau's grasp and emerged again, bright and victorious and glistening anew.

****

Apprenticeship of an Author

*C*awas Byramji stares out the window of his basement room and wonders where his inspiration comes from on this bitterly frosty Toronto winter morning. It is an unimaginative neighbourhood in a working class part of what was once rural North York, but is now ordinary suburbia. The chill gets into his bones and seeps through the cleavage of his ear like a damp newspaper fending off a blizzard. There is nothing here for him but provincial cold, supermarket and mall misery and stale memories. This is his life, this Cawas Byramji's.

***

I am a character in one of his short stories. My name is Rustomji and I dwell in a Parsee colony in Bombay, one that we call with affection a *baug*. He has written me up with much disdain and humour and bawdiness, some of which I approve, and some of which I do not. There are passages in my life which he has grafted from thin air, and some which are so true to the fact of the matter that I am forced to cringe when I read it. On the whole, I think that since he has taken the liberty of summing me up so well, and that too without my permission, the least favour I can pay him back with is to tell him what I think about his life, for a change.

However, being that I am a journalist, having spent much of my thirty-eight years in the service of the reputed and reputable *The Times of India*, I do not ascertain facts out of the abovementioned thin air. I dig for detail, I find faults in fiction, and I read and research my subject thoroughly before even one word goes to print. Although, I do not think in my heyday, when proofreaders were not the pillion riders that they are today, that that last sentence would have been approved for ink, because of the dependence on the alliterative form to convey the image.

Still, I digress.

***

The Air-India wing braces itself for wind-chill, pulls back its rafters like a dog snarling its teeth at a newcomer, and lands lopsided, two wheels then one, onto the glistening tarmac. It is midnight already, and the much delayed and harrowed cast of this endless flight make its weary steps into the terminal. It is abandoned and empty and wears a forlorn look.

I had a B&B room booked in a place called Hyde Park B&B, which was nowhere near anything called Hyde Park, and did not resemble the Englishness of its namesake. Still, the Polish immigrants in this beautifully cozy brick house on a quiet street in Mississauga, had the exuberant warmth that all backward nations exhibit. I was made to feel at home from the moment I walked through the door, because the handshakes were plump and vigorous and the smiles warm enough.

The morning woke me with its startling sense of light. It peered through the thin muslin sheets and pierced through the thick cotton curtains. The Polish breakfast laid out for me could have fed a small middle-class Indian family in Borivali. I ate with relish, wasting much of what appeared endlessly before me, as no amount of protestations in the universal sign language could convince my landlady that I had indeed eaten enough. After the meal, I indicated "telephone" with my hands in a circular motion close to the ear, and promptly understanding, she led me to it. An ancient white instrument covered with an intricately knitted cloth doily. Not since my Farzana departed these plains had I seen anything so much like home.

I called Directory Enquiries.

"Which city please," the operator wanted to know.

"Toronto," came my swift and proud reply.

"Where exactly?" she wants to know.

"If I knew where exactly, why would I call you?"

There is some problem with the line, as it gets promptly disconnected. I call again.

"I believe we got disconnected there. The lady was helping me with a telephone number."

"Which city?"

"Toronto."

"Where exactly."

"I don't know."

"What's the name?"

"Byramji."

I spell it out for her. There are three listings. I call all three. At the first, the name is spelt differently. At the second, a kindly old voice answers.

"Who did you say you're looking for?"

"Cawas. Cawas Byramji."

"Well, this is Byramji all right, but there's nobody by the name of Cawas here."

"But surely you've heard of Cawas Byramji, the famous author?" I retort.

No, he hasn't.

"Did you know you share the last and very unusual name with this author?"

He did not know.

"He just won the Booker," I tell him, "and he's a Parsee just like you".

"Who's Booker and what did he win, and what is it to me anyway?" this fellow wants to know.

Seeing a dead-end when I know one, I hang up.

At the third exchange, the pleasantries are more fruitful. The young lady knew all about the famous Cawas Byramji, and had in fact fended off many callers who thought hers was his number.

"Yes, yes, I know Mr. Byramji. It is a small curse to share his last name, but we are proud, nevertheless," she said in fluent Gujarati. "It is not everyday that a Parsee wins the Booker prize, no?"

Did she know where I could find the man?

"As far as I know, he is a very reclusive person, you know? Like all authors, I tell you. Rumour has it he lives in some industrial town, in some flat and boring neighbourhood in York somewhere."

"York?"

"North York, I am told. But good luck, as I do not

think he sees many people."

***

The sandwich is cold and heartless and frugal. Cawas bites into it with a certain premeditated plan. He has sorted out the corner to begin with, and holds the thin white damp bread in just such a manner as to ensure that its contents do not fall out. Then he chews methodically. His wife is having an emergency in the kitchen at this point, but she knows better than to disturb Cawas. He examines his long fingers for the umpteenth time that day, and scratches his beard gently below the chin, where it sometimes bothers him. He masticates deliberately, as though analyzing each chew by creating headings, sub-headings, paragraphs and chapters. Then he stares out at the snow.

Dilnawaz is fretting about the minor fire that has broken out. The *patrels* that she's frying require a particular method of cooking, which is only advisable back home, where not only is the correct oil available, but there are always ample servants and neighbours on standby for just such an occasion. She swats the small fire with a damp towel from the bathroom and swears yet another time that day that she should never have married an author.

"Ivory castles, I tell you. Ivory castles, with no approach road, a deep moat and a wall so high, you could see it from the moon," she was fond of saying when describing her habitat to the occasional friend or relative that did drop by. "These writers — if they can't hear themselves think, they'll go deaf." Then she would break out in a particular laugh that was neither sad nor happy.

Cawas finished his lunch, and scraped the breadcrumbs

off the table with the palm of his hand. He placed these gently in the wastebasket below him. Even from the corner of his eye, he could tell that it was empty today. That usual high-brow worried look came over him. What was it the English teacher from St. Mary's in Byculla had said?

"You want to become a writer, young man?"

Cawas had nodded.

"A writer or an author?"

Cawas looked at the patronly old teacher, confused. "I.. I don't understand."

"A writer just writes. But everybody writes something or the other. Poems, articles, gossip columns. Dear Diary. Today so-and-so did so-and-so at so-and-so place. Is that what you want to be — a writer?"

"Uhm... no I guess not. I want — I want to write books, and stuff."

"Aha! Then don't call yourself a writer, call yourself an author. There is a big difference. It's the difference between kicking yourself in the shin and blowing your brains out with a pistol. You understand?"

The young Cawas didn't, but nodded anyway.

"If you want to become an author young man, the first thing you need to get yourself is a very big wastepaper basket."

The English teacher pinched Cawas' gaunt cheeks, ruffled his hair and swept away with the air of someone who has just made the State of the Union address. Cawas stood on the spot, uncertain as to whether the teacher had heard "writer" or "sweeper", more confused than before he asked advice.

***

People call me Rustomji even though I am not that old.

Sixty years maybe six times too many but it is still four short of three figures. I'm a test batsman, none of this one-day innings business for me. I'm gunning for the century. The "ji" comes from respect in the old Indian tradition. They say it has something to do with the seriousness of my demeanor and the experiences I have notched up in various corners of this world as a journalist. I have been to exactly seventeen countries where I have covered everything from war to pestilence, from handshakes to earthquakes, from walls that went up to walls that came down.

But if you had to ask me where my home was, I would have to say Wadia *baug*, Parel, Bombay, because that is where my whole world exists. What I want to know from this Cawas Byramji whom I have never met, is whether the *baug* in his book is mine or some one else's. What I want to know is how he can write about a place that is ten thousand miles away at the opposite end of the globe, and pretend as though he were living in my backyard all the while that he wrote it? If Cawas Byramji did not in fact live in Wadia *baug*, what gives him the right to depict all our lives in so much detail, as though he did? Most importantly, I know from memory that I have never met anyone called Cawas Byramji in my many years. I am known to have an elephantine memory that has never failed me. I, therefore, also want to know how come he wrote an entire story about me that was so personal I had to buy every book in Strand Bookstore in order to stop others from reading it?

I think this man is an impostor, this Cawas fellow. What sort of a name is Cawas Byramji anyway? No self-respecting Parsee would call himself Cawas Byramji and still expect to be able to hold his head high during *Jashans*.

***

It had occurred to him only when he began writing his first novel, as to what the English teacher had meant. A compilation of short stories is just that — a compilation. A series of one night stands — all intense, furious, passionate, but over before it even began. All hack writers write short stories. All bad swimmers jump off the shallow end. An author closes the chapter on his real life as he knows it, keeps the telephone off the hook, shuts the doors to the house, builds the moat, and climbs a mile on a jet propelled plane and flings himself into the whims and fancies of an unrepentant wind, parachute-less.

This wastepaper basket metaphor came to him one day, just pages into his first novel. No longer was he satisfied with his words, with the thoughts and actions of his protagonists. More and more material found itself junked into the basket at his feet. The more he trashed, the happier he became, in an inadvertent sort of way. Soon, he was replacing his wastepaper basket for an even bigger one, and even then, the coffers kept filling. "Good writing", he was to later tell his wife, "I think I'm beginning to understand that it is more about what you throw out than about what you keep."

***

I, of course, know better than to make such a sweepingly redundant statement. As a journalist, I retain only what is fact, and trash only what is fiction. Good writing lies in understanding the difference between the two. But who am I after all, in the author's general scheme of things to be making such pronouncements? Just another character with a voice, but no spine, no dimension. At least the author has a small scruffy bearded photograph on the back jacket cover. What do I get? Nothing. He condescends to open my life up to prying eyes, to distort every detail, to magnify every little tweak and pull of my personality, and just because I don't exist, the author, in his imperiousness, thinks I have no rights. I do. I have just formed the Union of Harassed Fictional Characters, (UHFC) and I intend to start a signature drive.

I take the subway to the centre of town. I get off at the corner of Yonge and Bloor Streets. I am in the dead heart of midtown. Nowhere else does the concept of downtown and uptown make as much sense as in Toronto. Take Yonge street for example. So long, it easily qualifies as the longest in the world. You could run a couple of marathons on its stretch. East of Yonge is East Toronto, west of Yonge is West Toronto. Walk up, and you go north, and vice versa. Of course, no self-respecting Torontonian will tell you this, but allow it to the methodical planning and structuring of a journalist's mind.

I work my way uptown towards Dupont and Yonge and find what I'm looking for. The First Dominion Bank. I enter its hallowed ornate hall and enquire after the manager.

"Do you wish to open an account, sir?"

"No, I wish to see the manager."

"To what purpose?"

"To the purpose of seeing the manager."

"Is there anything I can help you with?"

"Yes, you can help me by letting me see the manager," I dig my old stubborn journalistic heels in and mutter.

The manager comes to see me. I am impressed with the service one gets in foreign countries. Not a nickel to my name and the manager of the bank takes time off to say hello.

"I would like to enquire after one of your ex-employees. A certain Mr. Cawas Byramji, who I am told, on good authority, worked at your bank for about twelve years, before he became a full-time author."

"Ah, Cawas! Yes. Cawas. One of our star bankers. Who knew? I mean, how could we possibly tell that somewhere in his quiet and withdrawn demeanour, we had a major international talent? I mean, yes, a few short stories here and there, in some obscure magazines, but the Commonwealth prize, the Governor General's and now the Booker! We were all astonished! And proud, of course!"

"Yes. Yes. But do you know where I can meet him?"

"What business do you have with him?"

"I just want to talk to him."

"If I am not being too impertinent, may I ask what it's about?"

"It's about finding out how he can write, sitting here in a bank in midtown Toronto, about my *baug*, in downtown Bombay, which is as removed from this world as *The Times of India* is from the *Indian Express*."

"I see."

There was a deep and profound silence between us.

"I don't know if I can help you in your search, because none of us here knows where he lives. He worked here everyday for twelve years, you see, but no-one really knew him much. Quiet fellow. He was very reclusive, you see."

"In that case, can you tell me something about him?"

"What sort of thing?"

"For instance, did he ever take leave and return to India to write the book?"

"I don't think Cawas ever took leave. He was regular as a bran fibre diet."

"You mean you think he wrote the whole book sitting here in this bank?"

"The first book — quite possibly, because it came out when he was still working here. Only when it became a major success, did he leave us."

"Do you not consider that wrong somehow, that he has the audacity to write about cheese while he's eating chalk?"

"I don't think I quite understand."

"It's like my writing a report from Bosnia sitting in Bombay."

"But he's not a journalist, you know!"

"But he wrote about my life! I have a life, you know! He created me, he captured all my nuances, my subtleties, the way I make my motions, the way I eat my *dhansak*, the way I tie my pyjama knot — everything. And he hasn't even met me! Do you not think the least decency he should have had was to have met me and said — Rustomji, I am going to create a character on your life. Please may I do so?"

"I don't really know. Perhaps you are right. But if writers only wrote what they know, after all due permissions, then what would be the use of an imagination? Of originality?"

"If it was just his imagination, then what am I doing here? Who am I, if I'm not real? Here, see, pinch me. I'm as real as the front page headline."

"Who did you say you are?"

"I'm a character from his first book. My name is Rustomji. Pleased to make your acquaintance."

***

If the first novel was like extracting blood from stone, the second was quite the reverse. He thought switching back to his Bombay of the 70's could be re-enacted by not making a new visit, which would only evoke current images and make him lose the old ones. Still, retaining characters from memory, road signs from childhood, fat aunts and uncles and maid-servants and the like was not altogether an easy task. What proved most difficult was this notion of "home" that he toyed with in the first collection. There, it was clear that home was somewhere between two continents, one foot in each, buried over the Atlantic perhaps. This was cause to create tension, to write dramaturgy inspired by the need to be here or there or somewhere, anyplace at all, where one could say one belonged. But the Parsees are the only ones left on this good earth who haven't a land to call their own. What else was he supposed to first write about except what it was like being there then, and here now.

With the second volume, the crispness of the memory was still alive, albeit flagging somewhat. A decade and more is a long time to retain details. Even photographs begin to fade into some cumulative obscurity. With the third, the "Great Indian novel", as the pundits came to call it, his senses had to be jogged violently. Two decades on, and he had spent more time in his adopted country, than in his own. How did he bring to life this absolute sense of detail? This visceral ability to capture make-believe people and make people believe that they weren't make-believe after all? Two decades on, and he still wrote about his "home" as though he had left but yesterday. How many lifetimes had he spent recording with those silent eyes, framed by large horn-rimmed glasses, the everyday goings-on of everyday people like you and me?

***

I, Rustomji (last name deleted for security reasons) am

determined to get to the bottom of this. Even my own erstwhile reportage has become tinged with maudlin emotion and heresy. For want of fact and details and "doing verbs" as my last editor so fondly called them, I have succumbed to the puff-and-pastry school of journalism, writing instead about inane details that any self-respecting reporter would not file as a story. This trend must stop or else I will be banned for life from the Foreign Correspondents Club, and be made to do without my subsidized Scotch whiskies.

***

I take a bus north on University Avenue Road, past Forest Hill and Briar Hill Avenue. I am struck by the serenity of the urban landscape. In my home, it is not possible to move anywhere without a million people blocking your each transaction, horns blaring, thickets and throngs everywhere. There life is lived in dense and intense spasms spent gasping for air. Here, the orderliness of the streets, the pedestrians, the cleanliness, and the open friendliness with which people greet you or even sometimes stare at you, is a welcome breath. I have been to many places more orderly, no doubt, but none that mixes progress with a certain home-town personality.

There are two Yorks. Both are North York, but are separated by Lawrence Park. I get off at the first stop at North York and am amused by how the passengers thank the bus driver for doing his job. I walk towards a corner shop and ask instructions to the nearest library. It is a good walk away, and I ponder as to whether I can make it before closing time. I look at the old handy wristwatch and risk my way towards it. Big brick suburban houses on flat land with narrower roads meet me at every corner. The traffic is sparser here.

I reach the library and ask for the head librarian. I expect to meet a grim old retired lady with rimmed reading-glasses perched on the beak of her nose. Instead, I meet a shaved-headed young man, with tattoos up his arm and muscular torso.

"Yup?" he asks.

"Yup what?" I want to know.

"Whadya want?"

"I want to know about Cawas Byramji. I don't suppose you know who he is?"

"Yup. He lives close by."

I have to sit. My hands shake a little as I grasp the back of a nearby chair for support. The boy has taken the wind out of me.

"You OK?"

"Yup."

"Whadya wanna know about Cawas?"

"I wanna know how you know him?"

"He comes here often. Reads. Sometimes even writes. One chapter from *Walking the Fine Line* was written here."

"No!" I exclaim in shock.

"Yup. Come I'll show you where."

He escorts me to a small cabin, unfurnished except for a desk and a chair. There are many like it in a neat line, like English row-houses. It is small, shabby and uninteresting.

"He always asked for the last cabin."

"Why?"

"Because it was quieter, since it had only one neighbour, and was stuck against the wall."

"What would happen if he came and the cabin was occupied?"

"He would wait until the person left. He wouldn't write anywhere else."

"Why?"

"I don't know."

I touch the table softly and close my eyes. I can see pages from the book fly past me like a trailer for a motion picture. They scream their potency as they soar above me, around me. I can see some people — the tailors, the old Parsee, the places, the mountains, the slums. The table is warm to my touch. I cannot bear to sit down. How could he recreate that world here in this breathless box? This square matchbox that doesn't even offer the hope of a view, the possibility of space? I am dizzy with the feeling. I leave the box and re-enter the mortal world.

The young man is staring at me.

"Are you a fan?"

"No. I'm a character from one of his books. My name is Rustomji. Perhaps you read *Stories From The Baug*?"

"Oh yes, of course! Rustomji! Funny. Bawdy stuff, yeah? I mean the way he wrote about you on the throne and all that ..."

"Yeah, yeah, I know. Don't remind me. I feel violated. Like he was there — some fly on my wall, watching every twitch in my movements. No decency I tell you. Whatever happened to privacy? To a basic by-your-leave?"

"He doesn't need to take anyone's by-your-leave! He's a writer! His job is to make things up."

"He made me up and I'm paying the price for it."

"How?"

"How would you like it if your life was written by some stranger and published in a best-selling book?"

"If Cawas wrote it, I'd be flattered."

"So you're a fan then?"

"Big time. I've even got an autographed copy of *So Many Journeys*."

"I'm happy for you. Now can you show me where he lives?"

"Nope."

"Why not?"

"Coz I don't know."

"You just said he lived close by!"

"I presume he lives close by 'coz he'd come here walking."

"I presume you don't have a hole in your head 'coz you're bald, but I could be wrong."

I don't think the punk got that. Still, I left in a hurry because I had no idea where that sentence came from. It was certainly not the sort of thing my colleagues at *The Times of India* would expect. Not at my age and with my status and decorum. This whole searching out this Cawas fellow is becoming a trifle dangerous and expensive. Already I have been here four days and although he could be living around the corner from me, I have no way of knowing. All I do know is that if I were to meet him now, I would have to call upon all my reserves to restrain myself from wringing his neck with my bare hands and seeking compensation.

***

His apprenticeship did not begin till much later in his life. Although he still doesn't know it, it was the twelve long and discipline-induced years at the bank that sealed his fate. Until then, writing had been a passion, a hobby of sorts. Something to squeeze in on Saturdays and an occasional Sunday when family pressures did not mount. It was the discipline that the bank was to later teach him that made him the author he was today. For he was to state enough times in his spotlight years that the second most important thing an author needs is discipline.

When pressed to answer what the first most important thing was, he would smile politely and remain silent. How could he expect them to understand the first principle of good writing as laid down by the English master at St. Mary's? To his silence, the response from friends and family would usually be to laugh out loud and say, "*Arre*, Cawas, everyone knows that the first secret is to have a patient and understanding wife!" At this point, a lot of back-slapping would go on, and loud Parsee guffaws would permeate the room. Dilnawaz usually took this as her cue to break out in her litany of complaints — "A writer's lot is a sorry, solitary one, yes we know," etc. etc. "But a writer's wife! What does she have to show at the end of the day for her patience and understanding? After all, you can't cook a Booker!"

Cawas Byramji never thought aloud. If he did, people would be amused and scared by the voluminous thoughts that plagued his head. His silence was always construed as introvertedness, but inside his head, there was a cacophony of noises and observations. His eyes were like pieces of scrap carbon paper, re-recording events in minute details. He stored and filed away these thoughts in some random, but well planned out quarter of his mind. The way a person sat, the way he got up, lay down, closed his eyes, moved his hands, scratched an elbow. These were never trivial observations to Cawas. They created the totality of his world, and filled in the silent blank spaces.

He had gone swimming once, in his earlier days. At a local club in York. Stripping down to his bare briefs, he couldn't help but think he was so out of place here.

The pool was crowded with mothers and their children. Some solitary swimmers were making long and purposeful laps. He was not a strong swimmer, Cawas, but he could keep his head above water, as he was fond of saying. Swimming was the one pastime he revelled in. Something about the familiarity of the water and the noises underneath it, gave him comfort. It protected him from the world at large.

On this particular day, a rowdy group of skin-heads were in one corner, ogling at passersby, and generally making a nuisance of themselves. Their banter seemed harmless enough, until Cawas entered the pool. Placing his glasses on a deck chair close to the edge of the pool, he splashed into the deep end without noticing them. In the water, without his glasses, only an innate sense of direction and hearing guided him away from other swimmers.

It had been a while since he had come to the pool, and the muscles were feeling the tension. The last few chapters of *Walking the Fine Line* had taken a severe toll on him and he had been depressed with the outcome of the story as guided by his protagonists. He could not shake this depression that had clouded him of late. He was unable to understand why events in his book had taken such a sorry twist, and was still struggling to come to terms with the sobriety of his latest work as compared to the relative bawdiness of his earlier material. The emotional fatigue had worn him down to the point where he knew if he didn't let go of his characters, he would break down soon. Dilnawaz had been pleading with him to go swimming at least, and to put it away for a short while, but only today did he pluck up the courage to go.

He had completed a couple of laps. The other swimmers were filing out gradually. It was getting late. Cawas could feel the tension easing out of his body with each pull and stroke. He knew he was going out faster today, and he knew he would have to answer for it tomorrow, when his body would refuse to cooperate. But the release was palpable. He kept going.

A few more laps, and an exhausted Cawas emerged from the pool, and went to retrieve his glasses as he usually did. Being the very precise man that he was, he kept them in exactly the same place every time and could find them within moments. This time, however, they were nowhere to be found. Thinking his tiredness had gotten the better of him, he kept groping with his long, bony fingers.

"Looking for these, Brownie?"

Cawas froze. Even if he didn't recognize the voice, he knew it wasn't exactly friendly fire.

"What's worse than a Paki scum?"

"Dunno? A blind Paki Scum?"

Laughter. Cawas did not even attempt to maneuvre or to talk to them. He hadn't seen them earlier, and knew, with his non-occidental background, that the rest was now in someone else's hands, and there was little point in resisting fate. He closed his eyes.

***

I find my way to the address of his publisher. These are the very same people who published his first compilation without so much as a check up on its authenticity. The office is in a swanky apartment building in downtown Toronto, just off the harbourfront. I go up to the twelfth floor and ask to see the editor. I proffer my old *The Times of India* business card, knowing that I haven't used it in years. A very bleached white man comes out, sleeves rolled till his elbows.

"Yes, how may I help you?" he wants to know.

"I would like to meet Mr. Cawas Byramji, please, one of your authors."

"Why? What business do you have?"

"I am a journalist from *The Times of India*."

"But he released his book a long time ago."

"I'm doing a feature article."

"Well, I don't think he'll meet you as he usually doesn't see anyone, but I could ask him if you want."

"Please. Thank you."

The bleached man looks at the secretary and nods. She picks up the receiver, rifles through her phone book and makes the call. She asks for the man himself, and after a few moments, he comes on the line. I can see the bleached man introduce the situation with much unction and care. He is walking a tightrope even before he has said a word. I hear him stammer and stutter. I hear *The Times of India* repeated several times, but clearly he is losing the argument. Gravely, then, with much serious apologizing he places the receiver down gently, and turns to me.

A shrug.

"Is that all I get after I have travelled ten thousand miles to come meet this man?" I demand to know.

"But you didn't make an appointment."

"Neither did he when he decided to write about my life."

"I beg your pardon?"

"Look, I insist on sitting here until such time as I get an audience with Mr. Cawas Byramji."

The bleached editor looks at the secretary with a glance

that conveys "one of those chaps". He had obviously been here before and knew exactly how to handle the situation.

"Be my guest," he replies, before storming back to his office.

I sat. There was nothing else to do. Occasionally the secretary looked up and gave me a matronly smile, the sort that you give to mental patients in a high security lock-up. I caught up on a lot of reading as all their about-to-be published books were on display. After what seemed like a few hours, the secretary got up to go to the toilet. I grabbed my chance. No sooner had the door shut behind her, I stole my way up to her desk and flipped through the phone book to the letter "C". Cawas. Cawas. Cawas. No Cawas anywhere. Then I remembered that the West was a far sight more formal than us Third World people, and so I looked up "B". Sure enough, there it was. Byramji, Cawas. 194 Metella Road, North York. There is a God after all.

***

It was the incident at the pool that made Cawas look back in anger. All he kept asking himself was "why?" He had brought the Booker back to Canada after eons. He was one of their protected sons. A gift to the country. A Governor-General man. He had single-handedly put this northernly backwater provincial Commonwealth place on the international literary map. And what was his reward? A couple of teeth missing, a sore black eye and a fractured rib or two. Why?

Would this ever have happened back home? No. Where was home? He didn't know anymore. What was he doing in North York writing about a place ten thousand miles away and two decades removed? He could never be Canadian, no matter the rewards. He could no longer be Indian, no matter the nostalgia.

It was at this time that he started forming the opinion that as an author he was merely a man who marketed memories. Who sold things as they once were, by comparing them to how they now are. It was at this time that Cawas Byramji started thinking about home. Perhaps it was time to go back. He had overstayed his welcome.

***

He opened the door for me one morning, long after I rang his bell. I could hear shouts of "Dilnawaz, Dilnawaz," but it amounted to nothing, as she wasn't in. Begrudgingly he came to the entrance, scratching his beard. As he opened the door, he was standing barely a foot ahead of me.

We stared at each other a long time, as though the creation had suddenly landed up at the creator's doorstep to seek a pardon, or some compensation, or both. I knew there and then that we had never met, yet he knew everything there was to know about me. Finally, after several excruciatingly tense moments, he said simply, "Hello Rustomji. Welcome to Canada. How are you?"

I plucked up all the courage of my sixty years and docked him a right hook across the length and width of his face. The ferocity of the blow made my knuckles crunch under the impact. He stood still and dazed for a moment, then crashed backwards with a suddenness that petrified me.

****

A Woman on the Verge

She sits squat-legged and doe-eyed and watches out the window. The gentle murmuring of soft rain as it lashes the panes. The night is encrusted with fear — circled around the city she has grown to adore as much as the arc lights. This is not Her room — this is not Her view. These are not Her people.

The starched sheets crumple with vigour and the stale cold food of antiseptic kitchens travels lightly down Her uncomplaining throat. The soft hiss of the air conditioner is Her only solace, the closest she can get to verbal company. Strangers come and go and offer remedies and palliatives. Sad, sombre faces of fans and queues of directors and former lovers. All carry bouquets of yesterday's roses and the day before's memories.

At fifty, she is no longer the way everyone remembers Her. Yet she is more. That face that captivated reels of film

in Her heyday. That mystique, that figure, were still there.
That voice — like too many bourbons and too many
filterless cigarettes went to work on it every day. Velvety,
harsh and sultry as the days before a heavy rain.

She was Spain's national treasure. Her icon for sexy
motherhood. Her rubber-stamp of wholesome youth when
she was young, and every generation's fantasy. She was
the original candle in a fierce wind. With a rare organic
beauty that fathers would swear by if she were left
unadorned. She was the country's most popular calendar
girl. Her birthday was a national holiday, Her face
belonged on stamps and Her legend lived on through
good and forgettable films. Nothing dampened the public
interest in Her. She was a legendary superstar of whom
it was rumoured directors swore allegiance in undying
faith and in thousands of feet of film. Hers was the face
that launched a thousand careers and shattered a million
hearts.

"Nobody knows what happened — she's just sick. Not
sick with anything anyone can cure. Perhaps too much of
a good thing. The Paradise syndrome. After all, she's a
Woman on the Verge."

***

He was a long-distance operator who became a short-
sharp focus puller. A keen eye for detail and an ear for
slander gave him the reputation of a Turk among the
Titans with his first few works. Short, stubby, over-
worked, under shaved, he wore the perpetual look of the
never bathed.

At twenty-three he was cobbling together odd bits of
exposed film on Super-8. Friends, foes and family were
subjected to his daily inquisitions, which even for Spain,

made the Spanish one seem like a basic question-and-answer session after a screening. He liked placing people in their places. Sit there, eat like this, look this way. Say these things.

He was never good with people in the way people are when they say so-and-so is good with people. He ate his producers for breakfast, his technicians for lunch, and his actresses for dinner. He was a man on a mission — in a hurry, and knew exactly what he wanted at all times which made him a frustratingly good director. Not *"increible"* in the way people are when they say *"increible"* in this part of the world, but exceptional in an off-handed individualistic style.

His manic eyes flitted about the vistas of life like a voyeur at an auction for invalids. His forte was the macabre, the sordid, the virginal non-narrative. His oeuvre though, all of it — was his women. He liked them on the Verge — and almost always it was he who took them there.

***

I was the perpetual *té*-boy bringing hot *té* to cold actresses and cold *té* to angry young men in a dressing-room in eternity. I was paying my way in a *pensión* in a Madrileño suburb, giving part-time English classes and serving as a Production Assistant on a Spanish language film. I had seen all Her films and knew each moment fluently. She was *mi diosa* — my inspiration, my reason for coming to Spain. I was in love with Her and in awe of Him. He was too much in love with his own ingenuity to know how much she was his only ingenue.

Madrid never sleeps. It is the world's party capital and nobody knows how to live better than Madrileños. It isn't the siesta, nor is it the *Sangría* — it is their common aversion to coming home before the sun comes home. I had arrived here hitch-hiking my way from Paris and four days and five nights later, was planted firmly in a *tapas* bar, washing down tid-bits of *queso* with Rioja red as wanderlust. It was in the *estudiantil* section and the night air was rife with pregnant possibilities. Too tired to even look for a half-way decent hotel, I worked my way down to the Plaza Mayor and watched a group of tired gypsies go through the paces of a traditional Flamenco. I lay my head on my *mochilla* by a lamp post and slept the sleep of a thousand human hooves tapping their brittle bones to beat like an ETA army on the rampage in Bilbao.

She was everyone's wet dream. She was the flashlight in the fracas, the middle woman in everyone's search from mediocrity to magnificence. Fame never rested easy on Her nimble shoulders as she paid a higher than usual price for it. She had seen and been through everyone from Buñuel to Saura and it was rumoured that she had more lovers than an insomniac has sheep.

There was the family. Strongly sewn like the tight patterns on a home-knit sweater. Conservative, apolitical, industrial, cleaner than the first snow, and as dysfunctional as an American soap-opera family — big in conduct and artifice and poor in communication. Landed gentry from the *Barrio Salamanca*, houses of Dali and Goya, prose from García Lorca and verses verbatim from Antonio Muchado. She read Spanish literature in American colleges and was star student at *La Universidad de Salamanca*, and would recite Bécquer and Neruda in the same breath, but with much less passion than Her inane one-liners on the screen. In a make-believe world, Her world was more make-believe than' most.

It was Take 22. She was naked in a bathtub since 7 a.m. the same day and Her skin was pruned like a date. He was unsatisfied.

"Too much. Too much. Do less. You're killing it with your eyebrows. I don't want pity. Don't seek it. Give me strength. Your eyes are squinting in pain, your eyebrows have done the *Tour-de-France* and I don't even want to leave Madrid. Less. Less. This is not Paul Muni in Scarface."

He disliked trailers and make-up rooms and spouted instructions instead in front of a fifty-member crew. Nothing was sacred. Everything was sacrilegious.

I served tea all day until my fingers rotted with the heat. When she asked for it, she got vodka inserted like a quick-fix opium pipe. She stayed in the tub — splayed soap-bubbles over Her spreading midriff, making small talk with extras and technicians alike to dissipate the tension even from a closed set. Everyone knew he was keeping Her in there on purpose, insisting on the perfect take, when in fact most felt he had accomplished it in three or four. It was his way. His benevolent dictatorship. His exacting vengeance on a love gone awry.

He wore his actresses down with a process that combined attrition with acceptance. His method was in his maniacness — in the sheer exuberance of what he did and the energy of his aura. His wry tongue scathed venom at everyone within spitting distance. His respect came from the oddball twenty-to-one chances given to his first few films, that rewrote the box office.

Take 23. Here we go again.

"Get me more towels. Rub Her down. She's gravelly like the Sahara. I need compassion from loss. From your rough-hewn texture. From your *rímel* smudging with your tears. You want what? Glycerine? What is that? There will never be glycerine on my set. Cry, bitch. Cry. Think of your sordid, miserable, lonely life. Think of your breakdown. Think of June 1. Think of your family. Where were they? Weep. Weep buckets like raingods obeyed. In the bathtub, tears swelling with the water, merging like slashed wrists in pink soap bubbles. An alcoholic, lost beauty, on the wrong side of a half century, makes love to mirrors and batteries. Where do you go now my lovely? Where do you go? Who loves you baby? Who does? Me? Everyone knows that. You? You can't stop hating what you see because you remember what you once saw. That's the scene. That's your life. Cry baby. Cry. Let me see it."

Who loves you baby? I for one.

***

She calls him from Her hospital room.

"Yes?"

"It's me."

"I know."

"Aren't you going to ask me how I am?"

"No. I know how you are."

"How am I?"

"Fucked."

"How do you know?"

"The whole country knows, except your family thinks it's their little secret. The whole country has also been told by your people it was me that did you in."

"No it wasn't. I know. It wasn't you."

"I know it wasn't me. How are the nurses? Any good?"

"There's one you would like. She's just your type. Fat and short and black. Half Jamaican I'm told."

"Good. Can I come see you?"

A pause.

"No. I don't think so. The family wouldn't like it."

"I told you I'm responsible."

"No you're not. It was... me... it's them actually. Them. Won't let me be me. They want me to stop acting, as usual."

"Will you?"

"Not unless you stop offering me roles."

"How fat are the walls?"

"They're padded. Very padded. I miss you. I'm coming back to us soon. Very soon. I promise. Are you being good?"

"Got warts on both my palms."

"Love you."

"I know."

He puts the mobile down and gets back to a shot without a flicker of a moment passing. Old stories. New movies.

Who loves you baby? Not Him, that's for sure.

***

For a white race, the Spanish are passionate. Maybe it's the inquisition, or the centuries of Moorish rule, or the crazy shadows of the Alhambra, or its Catholicism. But here is a First World European country with the heart of the Third World. It is warm and suffused with emotion. Havana is heaven and Conquistadors are communists in disguise. There is life ebbing in the cobbled courtyards and couples make out everywhere. In *Plaza Santa Ana* there is so much electricity in the air as to light a small African country.

Still — what I remember most as always is that the women were more beautiful than most. There is a freshly scrubbed down quality to Spanish women that makes me understand why Spanish men invented the Spanish Fly. They're like first rain. They smell of the earth. My nostrils are aflame.

For a man with no roots and no address and no plan — this seems as good a place as any to grow roots. Fresh *gazpacho, paella* in saucepans and mothers with moustaches. All Spanish mothers have moustaches that would make Greek grandmothers blush and waists twice the size of their Matadors. Do all Spanish women grow up to become their mothers? This is a thought that gives me cause for concern, enough to consider moving on already.

***

Pack-up. Washed down minus the cake job, she sits in Her Jaguar and waits for him. He goes through his last minute wrap-ups for the day and blocks the next day's work. Here's the corridor shot, here's the wall, here's the bathroom and here's the bathtub. He re-lists his requirements for the next day.

"Bathtub again?"

"Again".

A half hour later he opens the passenger side to Her car and hops in as though he never went away. They drive in silence. She has Her eyes glued to the road with an intensity that spoke Catalan in a Spanish city. She was about as welcome in his world at this moment as Franco in a bull-fight. An hour later they reach *Calle Serano*, in *El Barrio Salamanca*. Her dark glasses perched firmly on Her face, with the prompt air of someone who has spent too many years ducking flashlights, she enters Her building.

He closes Her door behind him as she enters perfunctorily. He grabs Her by Her hair and slams Her against the wall. Her head hits concrete and with a loud exaltation she screams His name. He slaps Her with a sting that makes his fingers cringe. He calls Her names. Names she wants to hear. He has Her by the scruff of Her neck and keeps slamming Her fragile head against Her fragile wall. Her Greccos and Picassos rattle like an auctioneer's gavel at a low-bid. He rips Her day's wardrobe down the middle, clean as a good take. It falls with haste to the floor and makes soft comfort to Her knees as they crash — first one, then the other. She exclaims again — His name. It is sharp and sweet and desperate. Her hair covers Her face. Her hair. Her face. A thousand shampoo ads and a hundred magazine covers.

He reaches his short grubby hirsute fingers down towards Her and tweaks a strand of that shampoo-to-the-stars hair. Her face shortens in a grimace and Her teeth pluck into Her lower lip, easing a plump berry of red that brightens Her pale pallor. She calls his name out again. He gropes for a thick clump of Her hair and drags Her down the corridor. She starts with a whimper, but builds to a scream — still his name screamed. His name.

Down the stairs now. Each hit hard on straight edges with a sharp staccato to his name. An exclamation mark, not a full-stop. He kicks open the door to the bathroom and lifts Her over the cracked porcelain edge of the bathtub and throws Her in. He runs both taps on full — like an avalanche of ill-intentioned snow.

The shock of the first burst makes Her gasp for air. More names now. Abuses and endearments in one breath. Abuses and endearments. With Spanish, you need to be local to know the difference. He empties the contents of a pink bottle onto Her pruned body, already shrivelled with too much stale water, and she is swathed in circles of air and soap once again.

He looks at Her — contempt and love. Both corrupted and condoned. Then he closes the door to Her bathroom and with one last scream of his name he bolts Her from the outside.

In the morning, he makes love to Her trapped within the confines of the cracked porcelain bathtub. He with his clothes on, on his way to work, She naked as daylight on Her way to his work. The I-Love-Yous come thick and fast and ever-so-desperate.

The green sieve of my veins throbs its uncomfort as I watch the actor treat Her as mince. Slaps of encourage-ment, knees on satin, that famous shampoo-to-the-stars hair dragged across That corridor, That staircase (built at the last minute by an irate art-director), That broken old porcelain bathtub with cracks like a river in spate. That gushing sound of angry water. Those exclamations! The turn of the key in the door. The proud "CUT" for a shot in Take Three not even Four. That embarrassed and humiliated face, wet in Her bathrobe scurrying Her way to Her make-up room.

I was in love with Her. I was humbled by Him. How could He do this to this woman? This national heritage. His lead love-in, live-in actress. That face a million Spanish boys saw just as they went to sleep with wet dreams and marriage plans.

I could kill him.

***

That night at the local bar near my *pensión* at the *Puerto del Sol*, I and the other junior unit boys discussed once again the meaning of life, love and assorted other impossibilities. The Spanish national endowment for boys under 25 seems to be solely the pursuit of unavailable women. The *sangría* is cold and the conversation animated. For Manuel, the meaning of life is simply Her in a bathtub and he the water. Sebastian wants to be the bubbles and so on and so forth. I am simply Her slave for life and matters need amending.

I have an address. Everyone has the address. Nothing accomplished there, but I also have the telephone number. Probably not Her first or second or even Her least important number, but I do know that the number in question belongs to Her. I ring it. Nothing happens. I try again and again until I know the number better than my own. No reply. Perhaps she hasn't reached home as yet. I find myself outside Her building. An old-world derelict, fashionably done up with every modern convenience, but still retaining its old worldliness. I wait. I sit on the ledge of the sidewalk and look up at what I perceive to be Her window. Nothing happens. Nobody comes. Nobody goes. Darkness appears out of nowhere like a fuse blew on the set. I sit and wait.

A car pulls up and halts. Even in the dim light I can see it is Him. There is a driver behind the wheel, and there is Him. Within moments, perfectly co-ordinated like a high-wire circus act, the car door opens just as she steps out of the building and gracefully, without breaking step, she enters. Long kisses rev the car up into the night, and I am left choking on exhaust and bile.

The next night I try again. I sit on a *terraza* obliquely diagonal to Her building and watch its contents like it were prey. Minutes before midnight, I see Her getting out of his car, and walking towards the large glass doors of Her building. There is barely twenty feet between the car door and the building door and I am across the street. I know that if I do not reach Her before she reaches the building, it is over.

I throw a few pesetas on the table and make a dash for it. I swing past traffic and throw myself headlong onto pedestrians who duck at the last moment. I see his car pull-off from the kerb and leave. I reach Her door just as she reaches it.

"*Señora*, a word please. It's urgent."

"Who are you?"

"Never mind who I am. I work on your set. I need a word with you. It's about him. It's urgent."

"What is it?"

"Here? Can't we sit somewhere?"

"No. I'm tired. Tell me. What is it?"

I grip the handle of the door and slide away somewhat so that she follows me. I look at Her in disbelief that it is indeed Her. The love of my life. Every paradise I ever dreamed of began and ended with Her. She was far more beautiful to this twenty-year-old at Her ripe old fifty than she was when she was younger. I held onto the railing for support, gathered every ounce of courage I had, and began.

"He's killing you off, Señorita. He's no good for you. Everyone can see that. We're all... I mean, myself and all the boys, we're all completely devoted to you — give us the word, we'll let him know what we think. We'll walk out... we'll do anything. He's using you. He doesn't love you. He can't love anything. He's not capable of it. Why don't you see that? Leave him now. All the genius in all the world isn't worth its weight on a rigged-up weighing machine."

She looks at me with a face only a mother could have

for Her children without it seeming patronising. With that doe-eyed pity and with unmitigated love. Then she leans Her husky breath into mine, and whispers in a manner that I had spent lifetimes dreaming of.

"Thank you darling. Everything you say, I know already. Some things just have no explanations. Be good now."

And with that she kissed me gently on the cheek, turned on a heel and entered Her building. I stood there looking after Her, dumbfounded. Her *Amarige* perfume merged with the unmistakable musk of his own and lingered on like the devil to the born-again. I knew I could never wash my face again.

***

"I'm quitting," I tell the Unit Production Manager the next day on the sets.

"But you can't!" he screams back.

"Why not?"

"Because it's an Anglo-Spanish co-production. We have a requirement to keep a certain percentage of the crew English-speaking. You can't just walk out like that."

"All right then, change my job."

"What do you want to do?"

"I want to be His Driver."

"Who's?"

"God's," I say, as I point towards Him.

"He's not God, he's an asshole with very big balls. Why do you want to be his driver?"

"Because being a driver is three letters short of what I want to be, and because you never learn anything from men with small balls."

"I'll see what I can do."

On the sets that day, her last day of the shoot, he completely ignored Her. Not a word. There was clearly no tension at all, no fireworks. You could see clear as a flickerfree HMI light that it had been a good night, and that things were going on OK between them. He just chose to ignore Her for no apparent reason the crew could understand.

It was a dinner table scene. She had spent the day preparing his food knowing that he would return from the assignment awaiting his usual fare of *pollo con arroz* and *flan*, made in just the manner he liked it. She had simply to serve it, and sit on the table next to him and inquire how it was and whether in fact he still loved Her. It was one of the most submissive performances I have ever had the misfortune of witnessing. She kept shredding before our eyes like cabbage in the hot siesta sun. She kept looking at him for what to do, and nothing but the most basic of block-shots came Her way.

"Walk from here to there. Sit on that chair. Watch him eat."

"Yes... but ..."

"Is the food ready? It has to *look* warm — not just *be* warm. Can't you do something? Why the hell are you the A.D. if you can't make food look warm? Is that asking for too much? Or do you want me to issue a flyer at the entrance explaining to the audience that since the food we're shooting is *actually* warm, they should imagine it to also *look* warm. Give me some dancing curls of hot smoke above the *paella*, like its just come off the stove. I don't care how you do it. The cheese has melted — its not crisp — that shows its old food. Details, my friend. Details. The devil is in the details."

With us, he was his usual intolerable self. Whether we

agreed with him or not, (and most often we unfortunately did), he still remained intolerable at best. But today, he completely ignored Her. Didn't tell Her what to do at all. Usually he was a physical manicurist. Every eyebrow and cheekbone had its place somewhere in the labyrinthine compositions in his mind. Not today. Today the cheese was more important.

When the scene rolled, I understood the devil was in him and never mind the details.

She doesn't know what to do. She brings him the food that has been prepared with much gusto all day and sits there helplessly waiting *Herr Director's* orders to do something. She looks like a hapless stray puppy dog, begging attention. Her husband looks at Her fawning over him and can't bring himself to tell Her about the girl back in Brussels or wherever it is he's posted. The food is straight out of the oven just as he likes it, with no time at all to thaw. Dancing curls of hot smoke ring every dish.

"You know that I like the feel of a scalding mouth burnt with your food," he mumbles his dialogue.

She has none. She just sits there like the housewife she isn't and says something under Her breath about how much she appreciates his appreciation of Her food. She looks about the room, unsure of what else to do, and the small twitches in Her mouth are just right, Her uneasiness is on the mark, Her wariness about the company he keeps is tailor-made. She's not looking about the room or at Her husband as much as she is at Him. That helpless worn-out, carpet look. That patheticness. That vulnerability that made all the Spanish boys want to devote their lives to looking after Her.

He tries another dish. It's not at a temperature he likes it at. She swivels the last of Her vodka-to-look-like-water and pretends everything is all right between them. He tosses the plate away.

"It's cold."

"I'll heat it up."

"It's too late. I have to go."

"Now? But I thought you'd at least give me the day. You promised. It's only been a couple of hours."

"I have to go. It's a new assignment. I'm only en route. And in any case, I just dropped by to tell you again that I am no longer in..."

She screams. "I don't want to hear it. I won't hear it. I can reheat it. I can. I promise. From now on... next time..."

There are no dialogues in the script... the whole crew is looking at Her. The script supervisor is tugging his elbow. The husband slams up from the chair, puts his coat on and heads for the door. She runs after him, pleading for him not to go. She falls at his feet. He's at the door.

"Please, I beg of you... from now on..." she screams.

He's gone.

With a gargantuan sigh she collapses on the floor and starts muttering gibberish — all manner of nonsense, whispered to Herself, in every inconceivable language. Frail, and mole-like she sits crumpled in one corner, and continues to mutter long after the shot has been canned. It was the Beginning of Her end.

It was spot-on. Even a lowly Spot-boy like myself could see that. He was a bastard, but a damn-fine bastard, that's for sure.

(*Él es un bastardo pero un gran bastardo, por supuesto.*)

***

The phone rings again, blaring its monotonous cackle to the entire set. He lifts it up, knowing from the number flashing on the small screen that it is Her.

"Hi. It's me."

"I know."

"I'm still in hospital."

"I know."

"How's the shoot going?"

"Very well."

"Without me?"

"Without you."

"Do you miss me?"

"I miss directing you."

"Are you in the middle of something?"

"I'm always in the middle of something. She's under the shower now, expecting me to tell Her what to do."

"You're a bastard."

"I know."

"I'm never coming back to you. Never."

"Fine."

He puts the phone away and goes into the shower, promising never to bring those portable nightmares onto the set again.

***

Manuel is convinced that they are not having an affair, but merely pretending to have one so that the gossip columns can start gossiping about the movie. Sebastian thinks that's a lot of *mierda* and that he doesn't need any gossip columns, and she doesn't need him either. That the film will work in any case because it's so far off the planet that people will want to see it if for no other reason than that they want to know how twisted minds work. We're arguing as usual, sitting at *Las Cuevas*, after a sixteen hour day spent carrying *té* and *refrescos* to the sets, arguing about what did or did not happen in those sixteen hours. All I know for sure, is that I'm going to kill *el bastardo*... before he kills me first.

I get the job. I'm to be God's official chauffeur.

We drive down *Calle Velásquez*, where I know, as does much of the country, lies the hospital with its most famous patient. She is comfortably wrapped between starched sheets and padded walls, with the gentle hiss of the air-conditioner to keep Her company. I know where it is He wants to go. I also know that he has not been here before, judging by the way he directs me towards it, being that I'm somewhat the foreigner. I fidget with the rear-view mirror and get a glimpse of him, sitting uncomfortably in his plush seat, sweating before the interrogation lights. He has the largest bouquet of flowers in his arms, and a gift all wrapped up neat and ribbon-like. But he sweats under that bushy brow of his, and there's no getting away from that — here's the world's coolest director sweating like an ordinary spot-boy.

My arm-pits were moist with condensation. I could see the brick wall facade of the hospital looming large down the street. This was my chance — probably my only chance to finally take things into my own hands and be the maker of my own destiny. I stepped on the pedal like my life depended on it, and flew past traffic, flew past shops and windows and buildings, flew past red lights and orange lights. I could hear him screaming in the back seat, roaring his booming voice into oblivion. I screamed back that the pedal was stuck and that there was nothing I could do. *"Espera,"* I shouted at last. We're in a Hollywood movie. "Hang on."

And I was James Dean just before he crashed. I could have wrapped his 500 Merc like so much wallpaper on a telegraph pole. I could see the headlines the next day. "Promising young director killed by foreign driver." Foreign Driver. Three letters short of being a Director.

Just then, I stepped on the brake and brought the carcass to a screeching halt. Passengers and pedestrians alike emerged as though from a ride at a carnival — all shook up. I turned to God and whispered my apologies and promised to get the car fixed as he went to see *mi amor*.

He walked the corridors to Her antiseptic airconditioned boudoir with padded walls. He opened the door, and the lingering few family members made like to block his entry. Security guards were outside sleeping for their siesta, and they were awoken. In the ensuing melee, no one heard Her say, "Papa, please I want to see him."

Papa blocked the door like Cervantes' *Don Quixote* would the gates to the Alhambra and said *"Quo Vadis?"*

She said it again, only louder, "Papa, please I want to see him. Let him in."

The security guards, the nurses and assorted other leftovers of Her family now congregated in unison to stop him from entering.

So she shouts now. "Papa. Let him in."

They stare at Her coldly. Even under the sedation, the injections, the blurring vision, the mind-numbing medicines, the brain-inducing palliatives to keep Her calm, she was loud and adamant, and there was no arguing with Her.

"Close the door behind you."

He places the roses in a large carafe of Her urine sample and sits by Her bed. He takes Her hand in his. Hours pass before a word is spoken. He can see in Her eyes a glazed dulling of medicines. The best doctors in the country were called upon for the job, but not one could agree on a common cause of ailment. Every prescription was different. Every treatment opposite to every other. No one knew what was wrong, but everyone readily agreed everything was. She was a walking-talking zombie — operating at half speed, on half mast. The best way to quell rebellion, to hide adversity, he thought, was through bad medicine. After all, there isn't a drug that has been made for which an illness hasn't been created.

They close the door behind them. He sits by Her side. Silence.

***

"I brought you something."

"Me? Show me. What?"

He hands Her the parcel. All wrapped up neat and ribbon-like. She puts it to Her ear. Nothing. She shakes it up. Nothing.

"It's a book."

"Close enough. Open it."

She opens it with those dainty fingers that have traversed their path down many an actor's face. Those fingers manicured like topiaries. The wrapping paper saved studiously for another day. The tape peeled ever-so-gently as to bare its hidden intentions. She opens the close-enough-to-be-a-*libro* present.

"It's the script to our next film. I'm calling it "*Una Mujer al Borde*."

"Am I the Woman on the Verge? The title character?"

He nods.

"Then... of course," she says, with That voice we've heard about before.

***

I fly on the 500, like chewing gum got stuck on my accelerator foot. Out the street, away from the hospital, through the neighbourhood, past the suburbs, onto the countryside and onwards as far away as I could — to get between the Devil and His deep blue sea.

...

The "A" Train

I set out hoping once more, to get lost.

It is a particularly hot and humid New York night and the platform at 200th street and Broadway was sagging with the weight of passengers. Everyone is in the usual hurry to get from nowhere to nowhere in particular, and so nobody gives the man with his underwear across his face any notice. He is singing for his supper, a makeshift tin guitar slapped across his shoulder, held there by twine and plastic and the machinations of necessity. He warrants a statue unto himself, right there on the spot. Every so often, he looks the odd passenger in the eye as if challenging him to question him as to what he is doing with his underwear across his face.

I shake a head in approval. Sweat beads are dancing their sticky feet down my spine. The "A" train pulls into the platform, squeaking its wheels into oblivion, and the

human crush is on. Packed like so much rubble in a tin
can, we head, unawares, to exactly where we wish to go.
A squiggly thin man with a wiry frame and thinning hair
grasps both hands together, fingers trembling, whispering
the Lord's Prayer. His eyes are beady and shot through
with fear, his knees scraped from too many church pews
with old satin on knee rests that have long since given
way. A large beggar-man drags himself on his knees
through the double doors and parks himself squarely in
the face of the timid man's prayer, rattling loose change
in a beat-up plastic coffee cup that has seen fuller days.
The Lord is deaf, no doubt, and reads very fast. The prayer
has accelerated somewhat. He moves on. More pickings
down the line.

She is large and cumbersome and heavy-set as a
bloated billboard on a crowded Times Square. She takes
two seats, but is allowed only grudgingly by fellow
neighbours, pressed as they are, skin on skin, rolling like
so much dough. There is a flimsy umbrella between her
thighs, grasped, choked, suffocated therein. I think of it
as her lover, drowning now, surfacing clumsily for air. It
hasn't rained for days on end, but perhaps she knows
something we don't. It is a small umbrella. Parts of her
are indeed going to remain wet should it rain. Which
parts, I wonder aloud.

A shiny rolling top is thrown at my feet. I step aside.
It rotates brilliantly, almost on the very spot, humming
like a humming bird with laryngitis. A broad fake smiling
set of old dentures that haven't been cleaned since the
diapers were last changed look up at me. One dollar, I
am told. A mere dollar and that brilliant bulbous ball of
sheer mind-numbing pleasure is all mine for generations
to enjoy with offspring and siblings alike. I shake my head,

no thank you. From his tattered plastic bag within a paper bag, handles stapled together like glue, sporting a dubious address in Canal Street come more treasures of the high Pacific seas. A midget car that flops over. A robot that becomes a plane. A man-eating dinosaur that doubles as a beer can holder. Used batteries, business card folders, fluorescent toothpicks. All for the picking. I move on down the corridor.

Times Square, Penn Station, 14th Street. They blur into one another like one long platform separated by names. Sleepy faces, tense faces, faces grasping bags and women with teeth clenched and pumps pointed. They come and go and come again and nothing changes. Except the names of the stations. Washington Square, Canal Street. The vendor gets off to resupply, no doubt.

A couple against the door, one hand firmly on her behind, the other behind her neck. She doesn't know this, but she cannot move. He shows her something. An advertisement for hair oil, 99.9 per cent free of oil. He takes his hand and moves her neck. She sees it. They smile. He moves the neck back. They kiss. It is a short, untender kiss. It is an oil-drill searching for gold. Mismatched. Misplaced somehow. I look for the strings above her head. There don't seem to be any.

The double doors are jarred open again, much against their will, and a large man with his initials carved across the back of his head enters. He takes up shop at the centre of the carriage and barks preambles to no one in particular. No, he is not homeless. No, he is not hungry. He has fresh sandwiches should anyone want one. He has a long cylinder outstretched from one hand, rattling change. I cannot help but think how like a natural extension of his body it seems. No, they do not have government money.

No, they do not even have their own money, so someone has to dig deep. Dig deep, bore into your coffers until there is nothing but blood and gut left to see. His voice is sincere, his demeanour calm and composed. No one looks up from their sports pages. The Mets have lost again. So what of it? No one looks up from the society page. Another divorce, another marriage, another scandal, another pair of celebrity shoes gone awry. So what of it? I am busy. Go away.

He does, eventually. Richer by a dime perhaps. Still, there are carriages to go, and miles to rattle before others can sleep. I stare at headlines now. In bold 60-pica letters of screaming, blaring headlines. A dog psychiatrist who slept with his patients, a serial murderer of seventeen prostitutes — he was lonely. A Bronx slaying of a family, gang-land style, whatever that means. The *Post* has a .38 photo front page. The *Daily News*, not to be outdone, what looks like a .44. The *Times* is concerned about human rights abuses in Cambodia and allergy sufferers who cannot take their pet poodles out in Central Park — all on page one.

I look up at the texts in the advertisements all exhorting me to action. Call this, buy that, go here, see where we're all headed to. Nowhere in particular, and getting there fast. Faster than the word. Haemorrhoids? No problem. Call 1-800-NO-PILES. Injured in a car accident? No problem. Call 1-800-LETS-SUE. Pregnancy clinics, abortion centres, hair dyes, five minute approvals, ten minutes guaranteed or your money back. We're on a roller coaster ride to wherever-you-want-to-be USA, complete with tacky midget billboards, paste-up models advertising their wares, and mayors urging the use of a condom — "Play with them, but don't play around with them." Thank you Hizzoner, next case please.

Some suits are off at Chambers, do a ten block walk
to the financial centre, after a quick thirty-minute workout
at Bally's. Pin-striped, plain, dark and sombre, they scurry
out, briefcases clutched for dear life. All sport the Long
Island tan, the marriage ring, the *Wall Street Journal*. Crew-
cut, cropped neat and blond, widely freckled, they
congregate together, with an easy look amidst like company,
a guilt that slowly envelops amongst the less fortunate.
The panhandler's stare is brutal and harsh. The judgement
chair is high and peopled with wannabes. Get off, get off,
the soapbox wilts under the added weight of presumed
means.

The busker, the singer, the noise-maker, all descend
like thieves after a potential bounty. Bad renditions of
already crucified songs. A makeshift instrument, a tin
drum, long fingers that traipse across thin air, puncturing
silence. Gimmicks, gasps, rap, noises. All churning its
cornucopian, elegiac cacophony into numb ears, some
already protected, hidden behind Japanese earphones. Not
a decibel sooner too, the beggar, torn and rumpled beyond
distinction, crawls out of his corner and mutters something
about Mozart and bad taste from terrible musicians. The
homeless advocacy woman is upon them too, trying to
pass out yesterday's sandwiches that nobody seems to
want.

Meanwhile, every token-paying incumbent, desperately grabbing purse and handlebar and sanity, juggling
earphones from out of briefcases and bags, is oblivious
to every commotion, save for that in their own lives. No
thank you. I have given before. In 1978. No thank you.
I hate the Bee Gees. No thank you. I've eaten already. If
thoughts were read aloud, who could copyright them?
They belong, somehow, in this netherworld, to the cumu-

lative mass of the misbegotten.

A lurch. A stop. A sudden, simple full stop. Darkness. Silence. Then a scream. A gurgle. Another scream, nearer this time. Panic. Sweat and panic. Noises. Footsteps scurrying like mice on blades after a sliver of imported cheese. More screams. Behind me, next to me. Beside me. Me. It is over. An announcement. Garbled. A train ahead suddenly stopped, or rocked, or died, or fell into the East river, we do not know. Emergency light. A generator. A collective sigh of relief. Hands out of pockets, out of throats and shoulder holsters. An arm, another. A leg, another. Intact. My compact, my stereo, my paper, my purse, my wallet. My. Glaring now at neighbours once thought friendly, deprived of the pleasure by the withdrawal of light. Frozen bodies in mid-action, unable to remove sticky fingers from whence they do not belong. Suspicion. Like so many headlines written in an invisible subtext.

Noses buried now. Under the East river. Fathomless, clue-less, noses buried in blood in black on white. Noses buried in cheap paperbacks and romance novels. Jackets garnished with red-filtered sunsets and men with strong upper torsos and women lounging in their arms. Eyebrows dropped in text, immersed in throbbing muscles and heaving bosoms and three-point shots from thirty feet. Eyes clenched together like knuckles, tight-fisted, avoiding contact and look. Eyes lowered into pages of anonymous love stories from exotic locations too far removed from the dark, noisome stench of deeply burrowed steel. Elbows tucked in so tight as to leave permanent impressions on rib-bones. It is the boxing stance, south-paw, and everyone is ready for the fight. Newspapers folded and refolded and folded once more until only one column at a time is visible to be read. The imaginary air space of the other is never infiltrated. Noses buried now until the inaudible whisper on the speaker tells us we have arrived somewhere, I don't know where.

Brooklyn Bridge. Yellow-stained tiles long since given up the ghost. Peeling paint. Naked bulbs hang from ceilings. The platform is one long sweaty face, dripping its cumulative anger and vengeance onto the tracks. Crushed bodies, superimposed into each other. Pale faces, dark faces, pocked faces, pimpled faces, crumpled faces, dimpled faces, starched faces, wide-eyed faces, blasé faces, tired faces. Faces without smiles, faces sweaty with the day merging into night. Faces that speak with the hope, the fear, the expectation of going home. Faces that speak sadly of those for whom this *is* home.

A swarm of teenage boys, chewing gum noisily, baggy pants scarcely able to hold their own, 200 dollar sneakers bright and flashy, sporting labels and signatures, enter the train. A ghetto blaster. They move from carriage to carriage, gasping air in the dense corridors of the night. They run across our carriage once more, jumping over planted feet, umbrellas, bags and bodies. The old woman with the afternoon hat with flowers in it, clutching desperately to her Channel 13 bag from as many years, raises her lips in dismay and frowns. She shifts uncomfortably on the spot muttering incoherent nothings to herself too soft to be heard, yet she makes her protest clear.

They are gone suddenly, onto pastures new. Her voice rises, as does the severity of her complaint. She looks around as though to raise support, but the faces are buried too low to respond. She mutters on. Like a parrot with loose dentures cooped up in a tiny cage, she repeats herself till exhaustion takes over. Another young man of similar attire steps up and offers her a seat. She looks away at first, far too much dignity to accept. He persists with grace. With charm. An irresistible smile, gold teeth and all. Even the cap comes around the correct way. Somehow pleased at the effort, or the attention, she accepts, but only because he insisted. She lowers herself onto the twelve inches of room, and nudges her bottom firmly into place, elbows and all. Not once does she look at him.

The next stop is Nostrand Avenue. She gets off. Someone else steals his seat. Kingston, Utica, Ralph, Rockaway, Broadway East New York. I think of the dozen or so that get off here wondering aloud what it would be like giving their address to friends and annoying telephone company people from far-off places. Broadway. No, not "Broadway", Broadway. Not the great white way. Broadway, in East New York. We used to have a great white way here too. Now its largely Black and Hispanic.

Panhandlers more than one could handle, come and go and come again. Some amused, some angry, some clever, some hungry. Everyone with hands outstretched. Some in pride, some in fear, some in hurt. A Vietnam veteran, sporting a badge of authority, is missing a leg. Another, a victim of Agent Orange; you can't see what its doing to him, but at night the pain is impossible. Beat-up cups, empty faces. Ribs protrude like year-long carcasses, feet are dragged across yellowed floors. Clothes blackened with the weight of time and shame. Smells too impossible to imagine away. A scratch. More scratches as lumps of dried and dead skin fall off black bitten finger nails. The skin purple and pink and new, with hope for fresh life still. Eyes sunken and hollow. All glint and life dulled by the weight of an empty cup.

I move from carriage to carriage. From seat to seat, from handlebar to handlebar. I drift lazily with the motion, to and fro, to and fro, like a pram in a mother's nervous hand. Through tunnels cavernous and never-ending. Past stations not unlike anything that went before, except in name or number. Past bored faces and outstretched hands and kicking scraps of yesterday's newspaper and empty beer cans. I reach the end. I can look down at the tracks and see tiny mice scurry away at the eleventh hour in panic as the train plunges forward, steel on impersonal steel. I see empty packets, strewn garbage and used wrappers. Like the proverbial journey to the centre of the earth, I am inward bound, abyss-clad, labyrinth-ridden. This is not what I thought Hell would be like. It is quite a civilized place, with names and numbers like Euclid and 88th street. I am being led there, flashlight in hand, guide book in the other.

The cold of metal on the small of my back. I dare not turn around lest it be what I imagine it is. I reach, instead, for the inside of my pocket and pull out what might still be there. A few crumpled notes. Spat upon, dog-eared, sold to the cheapest bidder of flesh against metal. I hand it over the top of my shoulder. He counts it lazily. About enough to get home and throw in a packet of cheap cigarettes too. He tips his hat, makes his pleasant farewell and continues. I don't bother to turn to see the face. I have been here too many times before and know the routine.

A muttered incoherence behind me. A sort of drive-by poetry. A sonnet-dispensing ATM machine. I turn slowly, expecting nothing. At one end an old bum is nursing the remnants of an empty bottle. He holds it up and stares at the open end against the light. It has deprived him once more of one last iota. He drops his head in sadness, hand still obliqued against a sharp light. There are tears. I can see them traipse across his face, hot and bitter. In formation. In ones and twos and finally, threes. He stammers poetry with a lust I envy.

He stands up with abruptness. Stands firm, tall and proud and sings the anthem. Suddenly, I am at a baseball game somewhere, with peak caps, and hot-dogs, surrounded by people who live behind white picket fences. His voice is pure and harsh, sans bitterness or rancour. He is standing amidst puddles of tears now, but the anthem continues. He bows, eventually, to an imaginary populace, thundering him with an ovation, and returns to his reverie. Back against the harsh steel, rotting feet against the handles. A stream of yellowed piss winds its way down his trouser-leg and onto a welcome floor, where it mixes pell-mell with his tears. The bottle is caressed close to the heart, the smile is wide, the eyes are shut in innocence. He shall sleep another night. Another night to remain alive by cheating death.

The worm tunnels its way out of the hole and into first light. The light is pure, somehow purer than I remember it. By comparison perhaps, with what went before. I find myself strangely led to the outward. Drawn, as if by sheer will, towards the double doors. I am escaping darkness and throwing myself, headfirst into the unknown. The rungs are weak and rusted with time and weight. One hand grapples with the other, I am climbing now. With the sheer will of madness, of longing to always be on the other side of whichever side I'm on. Slowly now. The climb is short and steep and plagued with uncertainty. I reach my head above the top and peek a glance. The wind whips its savagery through my hair. My eyes smart with the pain, the pleasure, the freedom.

I pull myself out and stand atop the moving train. It is whizzing by now. I can see the far end of it, snaking its way through a wasteland of a green and blue reserve. At the far end I can see the shimmering lights of the airport, leading me, enticing me, once more, to destinations new and unrevealed. A pelican, a seagull dive into the marshlands for fish. A flat, empty terrain as far as the eye can see and beyond. I am walking now, towards the front. My body is whipped backwards by the sheer pull and force of the wind. It is a vast sea, a vast bay. My eyes squint against the pressure. I can see the airplanes land and take-off bringing their scurrying folkloads to and fro, to and fro, like so many passing waves in the ocean. I remember. I remember looking up in awe, wanting to be there. A man with metal wings sprouted as if on will, with destinations too afar, too beautiful, too virgin. I had to be there, wherever it was. Wherever it was was always better than wherever I was at the moment.

I remembered the Bandra express train from Churchgate in Bombay. I remembered the North Shore line in Sydney. I remembered the Kowloon-Canton railway into China. I remembered the Trans-Siberian railway from Vladivostok into Ulan Bator and Moscow. I remembered the Picadilly line, and the Sunset Limited out of New Orleans. I remembered the Grand Trunk road, Highway 1 and Freeway 10, the Western Ghats, the Autobahns, the M5's, the Pacific Highways, the Route 66's. I was there again. Everywhere I had been before. It unfurled itself like a woven tapestry too long and too myriad in its many miles to be forgotten so easily. I kept walking from one end to the other, all the time remembering things as they were, remembering my chase forever to make them as they ought to be.

This is how it ought to be. The world beneath my feet, escaping it at breakneck speed, into a land, a world, I do not know yet. This is the way it is for once. All the people of all the world I had travelled so far and wide to see were right here. Under my feet. I walked across them, over them, showered them with blessings and curses and eavesdroppings. I was a part of something at last. A great moving part of something larger, something much more indefinable than I had seen before. These tracks were heavy with the weight of usurped time. Five years. Five years and more I have walked down narrow untrodden paths, slept under vast speckled skies, searched for an intangible. All those years swept by like so many leaves in autumn gone rotten and heaped for the incinerator. All those years. I was standing now, on top of the world, racing into it headfirst, and with open arms and open eyes. I was wherever I wanted to be finally. This was it. Every day of every pebble unturned, every moment of every love, every minute of every sleeping, waking hour. It was here. Somehow. And with it, so was I. Every road met here. Every river coalesced here. Every memory began and ended here. Every person I had met in my life came out on the roof to say hello. I worked my way to the top of the first carriage, shaking every hand, taking them in mine, until there was no one left, except me. I was at the head of the line, racing into where the ocean met the sky, and all I could do was reach a hand out, meet my other, and introduce me to myself once more. My journey had ended, I knew.

I was home. At last.